Sees the problem purely
biologically, no Christian perspective.

SEX IN THE ADOLESCENT YEARS

SEX IN THE

New Directions in

ADOLESCENT YEARS:

Guiding and Teaching Youth

Edited by ISADORE RUBIN, Ph.D.

and LESTER A. KIRKENDALL, Ph.D.

ASSOCIATION PRESS, NEW YORK

SEX IN THE ADOLESCENT YEARS:
NEW DIRECTIONS IN GUIDING AND TEACHING YOUTH

Copyright © 1968 by Sexology Corporation
Association Press   291 Broadway   New York, N.Y. 10007

Publisher's stock number: 1665
Library of Congress catalog card number: 68-11492

PRINTED IN THE UNITED STATES OF AMERICA

Contents

Introduction

In this volume, we have assembled for parents, counselors, and all who work with young people a collection of essays, each of which deals with one or another aspect of adolescent sexuality. As can be seen from the biographical sketches of the authors of these articles on page 10, each speaks with considerable authority in his field of specialization, and many are among the country's outstanding leaders in the field of sex research or education. All of the articles—with one or two exceptions—appeared originally in the Parent-Guidance section of *Sexology* magazine.

Sex education today is a highly sensitive area in which there is considerable difference of opinion as well as a recognized need for considerable exploration and accumulation of experience for some time to come. The authors of the various chapters in this book represent many points of view. They are united, however, in their belief that openness and honesty are essential for a dialogue with young people and in their opposition to the attempt to impose any rigid doctrines in sex education.

We have no hope in so controversial an area as sex that all readers will accept every view or statement presented. However, we believe that all the opinions represent the careful distillation of considerable thought, and will present a valuable challenge to the thoughtful parent or counselor. Dr. David R. Mace, one of the most distinguished leaders in the field of family living, has wisely pointed out that we rarely learn anything from persons who agree with us completely. It is the opinion with which we do not agree that stirs us to our most penetrating efforts, either in defending old beliefs or in clarifying new ones.

We are confident that the chapters that comprise this book point the way to many new directions in the sex education of the adolescent and offer an important new resource for the parent, the teacher, and the counselor.

—ISADORE RUBIN, PH.D.
LESTER A. KIRKENDALL, PH.D.

Note About the Contributors

Curtis E. Avery. Director of the E. C. Brown Trust for Social Hygiene Education and Professor of Education, University of Oregon.

Hugo G. Beigel, Ph.D. Secretary of the Society for the Scientific Study of Sex and Editor of *The Journal of Sex Research,* consultant in sex and personal problems, and former Professor of Psychology, Long Island University. Author of *Sex From A to Z.*

Donald N. Boydston, M.S., Ed.D. Director of Athletics and Acting Chairman, Department of Health Education, Southern Illinois University, and former National Chairman of The College Health Section, American Association for Health, Physical Education and Recreation. Co-author of *Teaching in the Elementary Schools* and *Annotated Guide to Free and Inexpensive Health Education Materials.*

Helen K. Branson, M.A., and Ralph Branson, M.A. Mr. and Mrs. Branson, marriage counselors and sociologists specializing in family relations, are both blind. Mrs. Branson has also done work with epileptic adolescents.

Deryck D. Calderwood. Now studying for his doctorate in the family-life field, Mr. Calderwood has specialized in sex education for teen-age boys and girls. He is Consultant for Educational Services for the Sex Information and Education Council of the U.S. (SIECUS).

Jordan W. Finkelstein, M.D. Formerly a Fellow in Pediatric Endocrinology of Johns Hopkins Hospital, Dr. Finkelstein is Assistant Professor of Pediatrics at the Albert Einstein College of Medicine and Adjunct Attending Pediatrician at the Montefiore Hospital and Medical Center, New York.

Robert A. Harper, Ph.D. Psychotherapist and marriage counselor, former President of the American Association of Marriage Counselors and of the American Academy of Psychotherapy. Author of *Marriage* and *Psychoanalysis and Psychotherapy: 36 Systems,* and co-author of *Creative Marriage.*

Warren R. Johnson, Ed.D. Professor and Head of the Department of Health Education at the University of Maryland. Member of the board of the Sex Information and Education Council of the U.S. (SIECUS). Author of *Human Sex and Sex Education.*

Lester A. Kirkendall, Ph.D. Professor of Family Life, Oregon State University, and Editor of Parent-Guidance Section of *Sexology* magazine; a founder and board member of SIECUS, and former consultant, U.S. Office of Education. Author of *Sex Education as Human Relations,* and *Premarital Intercourse* and *Interpersonal Relationships.*

Herman E. Krimmel, M.S.S.W. Director of Casework of the Cleveland (Ohio) Center on Alcoholism.

James Leslie McCary, Ph.D. Professor of Clinical Psychology, University of Houston, Texas.

Robert J. McDermott. Wrote the chapter that appears in this volume just after his eighteenth birthday. After three years in the Army, he is now a student at Oregon State University. He aspires to become a teacher or counselor or to go into some allied vocation in which he can work with young people.

Jerome S. Menaker, M.D. Practicing gynecologist in Wichita, Kansas, and Clinical Instructor of Obstetrics and Gynecology, University of Kansas Medical School.

Wardell B. Pomeroy, Ph.D. Director of Field Research, Institute for Sex Research, 1943–63, and now a practicing marriage counselor and psychotherapist. Co-author, with Kinsey and others, of *Sexual Behavior in the Human Male, Sexual Behavior in the Human Female, Pregnancy, Birth and Abortion,* and *Sex Offenders.*

Isadore Rubin, Ph.D. Editor of *Sexology* magazine and officer of SIECUS. Author of a doctoral dissertation in principles of sex education for the adolescent, and *Sexual Life After Sixty.*

Aaron L. Rutledge, Th.D. Leader, Counseling Service and Training Program in Counseling and Psychotherapy, Merrill-Palmer Institute. Author of *Pre-Marital Counseling.*

Richard Stiller, M.A. A former Associate Editor of *Sexology* magazine, Mr. Stiller compiled and edited *Illustrated Sex Atlas* and *Illustrated Sex Dictionary.* He is now Associate Director of the Information Center on Population Problems.

John B. Thompson. Professor of philosophy, California State College at Hayward. Former Dean, Rockefeller Memorial Chapel, Chicago University, and former member of the graduate faculty of theology.

Clark E. Vincent, Ph.D. Director, Behavioral Sciences Center, Bowman Gray School of Medicine. Member of the board of SIECUS. Author of *Unmarried Mothers.*

Part I

Sex Education in a Changing Society

MONKS OF MT. TABOR

1

What Real Sex Education Means

by ISADORE RUBIN, PH.D.

In his excellent book *Logic and Sexual Morality,* John Wilson, a British student of moral philosophy, describes a meeting he attended at a grammar school at which the audience of teen-agers and their parents puts questions about sex, religion, and morality to a panel of experts. Here were the kind of questions that came from the parents: "Why do so few children today seem to absorb what we teach them about religion and morality?" "Since we are all agreed that the Christian attitude to sex can be the only right one, why is there so much dispute about what to teach our children?" and so on.

The headmaster of the school was frankly amazed at these questions, for he knew the parents well. Very few of them were practicing Christians, and not one of them was absolutely clear about his reasons for and against various types of behavior. Yet in an instant they feigned a solid front of unimpeachable morality. One mother addressed this question to the panel: "How are we to teach young people today that the family must come first?" Three days earlier, this same woman had informed the headmaster that she was about to desert her husband for a lover with whom she had been having sexual intercourse for the last two years.

Under these circumstances it was not surprising that the teen-agers present asked only a few comparatively harmless questions, such as, "In what ways do the children of broken homes suffer?" Afterwards, however, Mr. Wilson was able to obtain the slips of paper on which the pupils had written their real questions which they had withdrawn when they heard the questions put by their parents. They contained such queries as, "Is it in fact true that men prefer their wives to be virgins on marriage? I don't and none of my friends do. Are we in the minority?" "Can you really know whether you want to marry a girl before you sleep with her?" And, "Aren't there some societies which are just as good as ours but practice quite different sexual moralities?"

THE PROBLEMS FACED BY SEX EDUCATORS

This incident makes glaringly obvious the basic dilemma faced by everyone in the field of sex education: Will he address himself to the real questions and problems of young people, or will he instead present himself as the spokesman of the status quo? Will he honestly and realistically concern himself with the needs of teen-agers, or will he see his function as that of catering to the prejudices of adults? He must choose one or the other, he cannot do both. Unfortunately, too many persons who call themselves sex educators view themselves not as educators but as apologists for the status quo. Accordingly, we would like to make it very clear that in this volume we are concerned not with indoctrination but with education. Now, rigid moral indoctrination has many virtues— it consists of a clear set of fixed rules and ready-made formulas, it is extremely easy, and it is highly pleasing to parents. But it has one small defect—it just won't work.

Most persons concerned with the education of young people will agree that without a real dialogue there can be no true education. But all of us should be prepared to recognize that having this dialogue does take courage, does present difficulties, and does present us with a real challenge. Once we open the door to a real dialogue with young people, we must be prepared to face the wide range of questions that they will ask. This is well illustrated by the lists of anonymous questions that are always submitted by young students to any trusted teacher. They are not childish questions about the role of the stork, but questions about the whole range of sexual experience. Answering them will not be easy.

How many of us are prepared to answer all questions honestly, openly, and in the light of the best scientific evidence available today? Most of us are not. On one occasion, Lester Kirkendall arranged a dialogue between students and a panel of high-school teachers. One student put the following question to the panel: "Suppose two mature and responsible people, twenty-four years of age, decide that they are going to have sexual intercourse for a period of time, being honest with each other and very careful in their use of contraceptives. What would be morally wrong with this?" When the panel finished giving their replies, the student was asked whether they had answered his question. His comment was, "Yeah, like they answer all questions about sex."

"An honest sex education," said Paul Gebhard, head of the Institute for Sex Research, "would by definition bring painful attention to the defects in our society's attempts at dealing with the sexual impulse; the problems we adults gloss over or evade would be open to scrutiny. If we adults find it hard to look upon reality, I doubt if we will permit the sight to our children." And yet unless we open up to scrutiny the real problems that exist—and that young people will discuss with or without adult guidance—we cannot possibly hope to prepare youngsters to cope with the real situations that will face them as adolescents and adults.

Clark E. Vincent, head of the department of behavioral science at Bowman Gray School of Medicine, has pointed out that those who argue against providing adequate, competent education about human sexuality frequently express the very naïve assumption that such education will encourage permissive and illicit sexual behavior. Curiously enough, this assumption is not made when we suggest, for example, the need for consumer education or physical education or driver education. We don't assume that these types of education will lead young people to become more permissive and foolish in spending money, or lead to abuses of the physical body, or increase the accident rate. In fact, records show the opposite. The more education, the more respect for finances, the car, and the human body.

We must emphasize that we are not mapping out a program of sex education under ideal conditions. We are discussing sex education in a society that is almost schizophrenic in its contradictory attitudes toward sex, in a world in which many old attitudes and codes are dying, and new ones are still struggling to be born. We are discussing a society where youngsters are given too much sex stimulation far too soon, where each day some new sex scandal fills the headlines, where each year perhaps half a million young people between the ages of five and thirteen are molested sexually in some way or other. There is no return to innocence; instead we must provide some knowledge, perhaps even prematurely.

THE IMPORTANCE OF THE ATTITUDE OF THE SEX EDUCATOR

It is clear that the basic attitude of the sex educator is of crucial importance; this will determine the purpose, content, and method of his guidance. If he holds an essentially negative attitude toward sex, his major efforts will be directed toward limiting and cutting down on every form of sex expression. If he holds an essentially affirmative attitude, his major efforts will be directed toward encouraging sex expression as a rich and positive aspect of life.

THE GOAL OF SEX EDUCATION

Sex education is *not* merely a unit in reproduction, teaching how babies are conceived and born. It has a far richer scope and goal: to help the youngster incorporate sex most meaningfully into his present and future life, to provide him with some basic understanding of virtually every aspect of sex by the time he reaches full maturity, to help him to recognize the existence of differential sex patterns so that he can interact harmoniously with those whose sex norms differ from his own, and to teach him critical judgment in dealing with ethical controversy. Thus the aim of sex education should be to indicate the immense possibilities for human fulfillment that sexuality offers, rather than primarily to control and to suppress sex expression.

This approach indicates the broad scope of sex education. At the same time, we should be very realistic about the limits of sex education. No educator can undertake to change the moral climate of his community, or to cut down the rate of illegitimacy or venereal disease. These social ills are the responsibility of society as a whole; no one agency can cure what society as a whole permits. Sex education based on this perspective is foredoomed to failure.

We must be realistic too about what we can accomplish for any one individual. Basically, sex education for the teen-ager is a process of emotional re-education. Certainly to change attitudes which have been rooted in childhood, reflect centuries of social conditioning, and are even today reinforced by sanctions of law and public opinion requires a process of re-education. In many cases, special counseling and therapy are required to effect any change. Tenacious attitudes cannot be altered by a casual, superficial sex education but only by a process of serious education conceived in reconstructive terms.

If we are to have a real dialogue with youth, we must recognize it as a two-way process. If we expect youth to listen to their elders, the elders must, in turn, listen to the adolescent. Not all of youth's sex behavior is an immature revolt against our moral codes. Some of it is a revolt against adult hypocrisy and a groping effort to find a morality that is meaningful in their world.

It is the beginning of wisdom in sex education to recognize that we are going through a great ordeal of transition in which we must learn to live with a bewildering array of alternative and conflicting value systems of sex, where each individual must make many ethical choices. In such a situation the educator can no longer provide "ready-made formulas and prepackaged values," but rather must teach the skills and attitudes for intelligent decision-making in a changing society.

REPLACING FEAR WITH FREEDOM

Unfortunately, in the past we attempted to build our morality—and our philosophy of education—on fear. Although we know now that this never really worked—and surely will work less and less as the bases for fear are more and more removed—we are unwilling to cut ourselves loose from our past and make the drastic modifications in our education that are necessary in an open society where different value systems exist side by side. In our old preoccupation with instilling fear and trying vainly to prevent any kind of sexual expression by young people, we neglected almost entirely to work out with them—in terms meaningful to them—the great new responsibilities that are thrust upon them by their new freedoms. We have to find a way of impressing upon adolescents and young adults that freedom is much more difficult to cope with than restriction, that every choice involves a dilemma, a weighing of the positive and negative consequences of every course of action. It is our responsibility to see that this choice is made with as much careful weighing and balancing as they are capable of, and with as much insight as we can give them into their own stage of maturity, their own ego needs, and their own as well as society's value system. This method of education will not be easy to achieve, but it will, in the long run, pay the richest dividends.

2

A Balanced View of "The Sexual Revolution"

by ISADORE RUBIN, PH.D.

A meaningful dialogue with young people—that is to say, a meaningful kind of sex education—can only take place if parents and educators are willing to face social reality and avoid the trap that every older generation falls into: the belief that the younger generation is "going to the dogs" because of the changes that inevitably occur between generations, particularly in a dynamic society such as ours.

Unfortunately, most persons—including professionals in the field of sex education—have been prevented from honestly facing the realities around them by a whole mythology that has sprung up about "uninhibited teen-age sex," particularly on the college campus. The foundation of this mythology rests upon a tired and over-worked phrase that has become a cliché that stifles thinking: "the sexual revolution." This cliché is a banner that serves the prophets of doom and the enthusiastic standard-bearers of sexual freedom equally well. Under this banner we have been told that the old patterns of morality and of sexual behavior are "in an advanced state of decay" and are losing ground with "dizzying rapidity."

THERE HAS BEEN NO REAL REVOLUTION
IN SEXUAL BEHAVIOR

And yet, in spite of all the easy clichés, a revolution in sexual behavior has not in fact occurred. This is the carefully reasoned conclusion of those experts who have made the most careful study of sexual patterns since the revelations of the first Kinsey Report.

The real revolution that has occurred is not so much in behavior as in the openness that has replaced much—but by no means all—of our traditional "hush and pretend" about sex and in the considerable changes that have taken place in sexual attitudes. These changes are very important, but they in no way add up to the popular concept of the tremendous change in behavior and morals that has supposedly taken place since the publication of the Kinsey Reports in 1948 and 1953.

If this is true, then we all have been highly irresponsible in swallowing this term whole and failing to analyze critically its how, when, where, and who, because the question of whether or not a revolution in sexual behavior has actually taken place is not merely one of theoretical interest to scholars; it also has far-reaching implications for behavior. For example, college men and women, bombarded on all sides by a stereotyped version of revolution, may come to feel that unless they hurry up and join this movement, they are hopelessly "square"—the lone exceptions perhaps on a campus that is teeming with sex activity. As a result, many boys and girls may be pressured into sexual relationships for which they are not yet emotionally or socially prepared.

STUDIES INDICATE THAT NO SEXUAL REVOLUTION HAS OCCURRED AMONG YOUNG PEOPLE

Those who believe that a revolution has occurred generally speak of an increase of promiscuous intercourse among young persons, particularly middle-class girls, an increase in extramarital intercourse among adults, and a sharp rise in male homosexuality.

However, as John H. Gagnon, a research specialist at the Kinsey Institute for Sex Research, has pointed out, there is no body of evidence to indicate figures sufficiently different from the Kinsey research data to justify any belief that basic changes have occurred in any of these three areas. The few careful research studies done since Kinsey do not basically indicate that girls are having intercourse far more often, or with far more partners, or with far less emotional commitment and affection than those studied a generation earlier. No responsible study has indicated that more than a very small percentage of girls are promiscuous. It is true that increasing numbers of girls pet to orgasm in an increasing number of ways, while remaining technically virgins. But intercourse for the vast majority of those who do engage in premarital coitus still does not take place until the girl is in love and is formally or informally committed to marriage. There is apparently an increase in such premarital intercourse, and it takes place earlier because of earlier marriage, but since it still remains within the context of impending marriage, it cannot be described as a basic change in sexual patterns.

Notice, of course, that the minute one starts analyzing the sexual revolution, one starts, almost without thinking, talking about girls, and primarily middle-class girls. No one tries seriously to argue that a vast change has occurred in the extent to which young men and boys engage in sexual activity, or that their basic attitudes toward sex have changed.

There is no doubt that homosexuality has increased tremendously in public discussion and in public obviousness. Once described as "the abominable sin not to be named among Christians," homosexuality is clearly evident wherever one turns. It is a subject of considerable preoccupation in the mass media and in the literary arts. At one time, almost all homosexuals kept their sexual orientations a matter of utmost secrecy. A. E. Housman, the British classical scholar and poet famous for *The Shropshire Lad,* took his secret to the grave with him, requesting that his homosexuality be made known only long after his death. Today, when a writer such as Somerset Maugham dies, his homosexuality is proclaimed as a matter of public record.

Today, too, a large number of openly homosexual organizations exist in the United States, and most have their own publication. Public conventions of Lesbians and male homosexuals are held, and picket lines are organized to protest their exclusion from State Department jobs and from the armed services. But does all this prove in any way that there are proportionately more homosexuals today (taking into account the population increase) than there were in 1948 when the first Kinsey figures were made public? Not at all. It merely proves that there are more homosexuals today who openly admit their homosexuality, and the subject itself is more freely discussed.

WHAT STUDIES OF PREMARITAL SEX SHOW

Let's take a look at some of the more careful research that has been done since Kinsey concerning the extent of premarital intercourse. One of the best studies appeared in England in 1965. It was a study of the sexual behavior of young people aged fifteen to nineteen conducted by Michael Schofield for the Central Council for Health Education. Although the number of young people involved was not the largest that had been investigated (1,873), it was the first large-scale survey of sex behavior of the general population taken anywhere where the sample was based on what is known statistically as a random sample, one that was designed to guarantee that a representative cross section of young people would be interviewed. In one small area of London, for example, one in every three teen-agers was in the sample.

By the age of eighteen, according to the results of this careful survey, a third of the boys and about a sixth of the girls had experienced sexual intercourse at least once. Only about 2 per cent of all the girls had had intercourse with more than one sexual partner during the entire previous year. For boys the figure was larger (about 12 per cent). These results suggest that although promiscuity exists among young people it is not a prominent feature of teen-age sexual behavior, certainly not of girls. As in most other careful studies, a sharp difference between the attitudes of boys and girls was noted: "The girl is looking for a romantic relationship while the boy is seeking a sexual relationship."

These results certainly do not support the common stereotype of teen-age immorality or of behavior which is sharply at variance with that of the previous generation. True, this study was conducted in England and the results cannot be mechanically applied in the United States. However, the findings are sufficiently similar to studies made in this country, and cultural conditions are sufficiently similar, to be strongly suggestive.

In the United States one of the most careful surveys of the behavior of college girls was a little-publicized report released in January, 1965, by Mervin B. Freedman. After a detailed study of an Eastern women's college for four years, Freedman found that more than 75 per cent of the unmarried women remained virgins; that premarital intercourse where it did take place was usually restricted to the future husbands; and that promiscuity was confined to a very small percentage of college women. While attitudes toward sex are often liberalized in college, Freedman concluded that "The Puritan heritage has by no means passed from the scene. . . . It is probable that the incidence of nonvirginity among college women has increased . . . little since the 1930's." It is important to note that Freedman's study was unique in that the subjects who were interviewed in depth were not volunteers, as in other studies, but comprised a careful sample of the student body, and the test data were based on whole classes of students.

Professor Nevitt Sanford, director of Stanford University's Institute for the Study of Human Problems, reported similar results from a survey of three women's colleges in different parts of the country. He noted that between 20 and 35 per cent of the women studied were not virgins at the time of graduation. The rates for young men were somewhat higher, but not substantially different from those for the women. "The general picture," he concluded, "is in line with that offered in the Kinsey report."

Both of these researchers conclude that no "sex revolution" is sweeping the American campus and that there has been "no decline in student morality." Their figures do not differ radically from other careful studies—by Winston W. Ehrmann and other researchers.

Compare Freedman's careful sample with the kind of sample interviewed by Gael Greene in her widely publicized *Sex and the College Girl*, which does not present any figures but conveys a totally different impression of the typical college girl. For her study, Miss Greene interviewed an average of six girls on each of one hundred and two different college campuses. Undoubtedly, girls such as she described do exist in some number on our college campuses. However, the important point is not whether they exist but how representative they are, and neither Gael Greene nor the reader can draw any conclusions about this due to the inadequate sample offered. As Clark Vincent points out, an interviewer could talk to half a dozen girls at each of twenty colleges and conclude sex had broken wide open and then come back and choose another set of six girls at each college and conclude that this is an "age of prudery."

Thus when a sociologist like Max Lerner asserts authoritatively in his introductory remarks to *Sex and the College Girl* that the world of the college girl "is that of motels, parked cars, drive-in movies, fraternity houses, dormitory rooms during 'parietal' hours, apartments loaned for the weekend. . . . It is a world of buzzing booming internal confusion, of sex without bed, of bed without love, of hedonism without joy," in the words of Chatham College President Edward D. Eddy, "he should know better."

BIRTH CONTROL AND THE SEX REVOLUTION

There is also the popular assumption that even if a revolution in behavior did not take place right after the Kinsey Report, it must now be in full swing because of "the pill." However, this belief too is based upon certain suppositions that do not hold up under careful examination. The basic assumption is that the sexual orientation and attitudes of the young adult can be easily reversed. In view of the great difficulty of changing most forms of behavior, said John Gagnon, "there seems to be a curious contradiction in the belief that sexual behavior is immediately amenable to change from the slightest external impulse."

If, as most psychiatrists and students of child development agree, adult sexual attitudes and behavior are deeply rooted in experiences in infancy and childhood, there is no reason to believe that the present generation of young people either directly or indirectly were conditioned by their parents with fewer inhibitions or less negative learning about sex than their parents themselves received. Certainly when they get older, most girls are not encouraged to be too permissive. As one study of college mothers and daughters (by Robert R. Bell and J. V. Buerkle) found, even those mothers who had been quite permissive themselves during their own courtship days became far less permissive when it came to their daughters.

Another assumption is that great changes in sexual behavior will follow hard upon changes in technology of birth control. But as Ira L. Reiss, one of the leading researchers into premarital sexual standards, has noted, the female diaphragm came into use starting in the 1880's and the male rubber protective device was perfected even earlier. Yet these methods hardly seem to have produced immediate radical changes in premarital coital participation. The changes in sexual standards and behaviors during this period seemed much more related to more basic facts of our social and cultural structure than to available contraceptive techniques, particularly upon the values of our society.

Actually, the greatest change in premarital sex behavior (as documented by the Kinsey research) took place just after World War I and during the 1920's—a period during which no essential advance in contraceptive techniques or knowledge occurred. This period, incidentally, is the one most deserving of the description "sexual revolution," and it may be a sobering thought to realize that this revolution was made not by today's teen-agers, but by today's grandmothers over sixty years of age. No increase in any way approaching the increase at that time (a jump of the percentage reporting premarital intercourse from an average of 14 to over 36 per cent) has since been noted.

If behavior depended primarily on contraceptive knowledge and techniques, the better-educated and higher-income groups to whom such knowledge has always been more available should have higher rates of premarital intercourse—whereas in fact the opposite seems to be true, according to the best available data. Many girls of course are using the pills. However, to believe that the pills have been able to bring about a great change in the attitudes and behavior of the vast majority of girls would be contrary to the present evidence for the motives of human behavior. It is true that the perfection of a foolproof and esthetically pleasing contraceptive deprives many persons of their major argument against premarital sex—fear of pregnancy—and that it may in the long run effect important changes in our value system relating to sex, but this "long run" may well be a matter of generations.

THE RISES IN VENEREAL DISEASE AND ILLEGITIMACY AND THEIR RELATION TO THE SEX REVOLUTION

Two other sets of figures are often cited to justify the belief in a sex revolution—the dramatic rises in venereal disease and the rate of illegitimacy. Proponents of this view insist that these figures must reflect a sharp rise in promiscuous intercourse, particularly among the young.

The trouble with citing VD figures—which have risen sharply since 1957 (please note the base date carefully)—is that they bear no direct relationship to the extent of promiscuous sexual relations. They are related only to the extent of sexual relations *taking place with partners who have venereal disease.* Thus the ups and downs of the charts plotting the extent of VD reflect success or failure in controlling these diseases rather than the changes in morality. To see the changes as correlated with an increase or decrease in morality would put us in the absurd position of arguing that the greatest drop in promiscuity in our history occurred in the period from the publication of the Kinsey Report on the male to the publication five years later of the Kinsey Report on the female. For it was 1947 that saw the highest figures on VD (far, far higher than those of today) and 1953 that saw the figures reach so low a point that our health services let down their guard and paved the way for a rise a few years later. Let us not lose sight of the fact that despite all the publicity about the rise in VD in recent years, the rate is still far below that of 1940.

When we come to the figures on the rise in illegitimacy, we are faced with a more difficult problem. There is no doubt that there has been a considerable rise in the number of illegitimate births in the past twenty-five years. However, even here it is difficult to draw any definite conclusions about its direct relationship to promiscuity, because of the selective kind of information which we have. For example, Clark Vincent, author of *Unmarried Mothers,* points out that much of the apparent increase in Negro illegitimacy may be due to the fact that a larger proportion of Negro illegitimacy may now be reported than in the past when more illicit births probably took place at home attended by a midwife, relative, or friend. In addition, white girls often go to one of the fifteen states that do not report illegitimacy or enter it on birth certificates.

At any rate, Vincent notes, our great emphasis on "young" unwed mothers is misleading, since the illegitimacy rate increased *least* among fifteen- to nineteen-year-olds in the last twenty-five years. (The rate of increase among those twenty-five to thirty-four years of age was more than four times greater than the rate of increase among teen-agers.) Also, it is important to realize that the most reliable indication of change is the *illegitimacy rate,* which is the number of illegitimate births per thousand unmarried females of child-bearing ages. Total numbers can be quite deceptive. Thus, for example, in the years from 1957 to 1963 (the latest year for which we have figures), the total number of illegitimate births in the fifteen- to nineteen-year-old group jumped considerably because of the "baby boom" of 1945–7. But the actual illegitimacy rate for that age group *decreased* 2 per cent! (The rate of increase for those twenty and older ranged from 9 to 31 per cent.)

CONCLUSION—A REVOLUTION IN OPENNESS NOT BEHAVIOR HAS TAKEN PLACE

To sum up then, we can find no reliable evidence either that a "revolution" in sex behavior has occurred since the Kinsey Reports or that any change is beginning to take place with "dizzying rapidity." In 1938, it is worth recalling, L. M. Terman, who is best known for his work on I.Q. tests but who was also one of the famous precursors of Kinsey, predicted that by 1960 the female virgin at marriage would be virtually extinct. The failure of this prediction, like so many other predictions of future events, should make us wary of overestimating the pace of sexual change.

How then can we explain the almost universal belief that a sexual revolution has occurred since the publication of the Kinsey Reports? Since sexual behavior has always been so private, John Gagnon points out, sexual experiences are often repressed: any information that is given about such behavior often comes as a great surprise. In addition, the great shifts that had taken place in the patterns of female sexual behavior since the Victorian era were never clearly realized. The publication of all this information in the Kinsey Reports came as a great shock to most people. They got the impression not that the events were merely being made public for the first time, but that for the first time such behavior was actually occurring. Because it has been only a few years since we have been delivered from a private to a public concept of sex, we are still in the process of discovering ourselves.

Thus for most people a revolution in sex behavior has been confused with a revolution in the openness with which we now talk publicly about our behavior. Much of the conviction about the sexual revolution flows from what Paul H. Gebhard has called the "terrific amount of verbalization about sex." Never before in our history or in the history of any country has there been so much talk about sex—on our campuses, in all our mass communications media, in our pulpits, in fact wherever literate (or illiterate) citizens or worried parents get together. Any newspaper editor knows how easy it is—merely by deciding to play up prominently some of the details of crimes that are always occurring—to create a "crime wave." In just such a way has a "sex revolution" in behavior been created.

But we would be fooling ourselves if we denied that important changes *have* taken place. "There is no way of proving that the present is morally inferior to the past," Walter Lippmann has said. "The big change is that while our conduct may not be any worse we are much more lax in what we think about our conduct." In the Victorian past, it was only the rare person who publicly challenged the official sex codes. No matter how often these codes were violated covertly in private, in public discussion virtually everyone felt it necessary to subscribe to them. Some people did so out of an honest belief that these codes represented the best social answer to the difficult problem of controlling the powerful sex impulse, regardless of their own or others' personal weaknesses; some did so out of lack of courage to swim against the overwhelming tide; but most simply reflected the traditionally morbid, guilt-ridden attitude toward sex that saw all "carnal lust" as basically sinful, to be accepted grudgingly even within the marriage bed.

However, as the twentieth century progressed, a basic shift began to take place throughout our culture "from sex denial to sex affirmation," as Evelyn M. Duvall has put it. As this shift took place, statements about moral beliefs more and more became divorced from realistic conduct. For larger and larger numbers, support of the official sex codes became mere ritualistic lip service; men and women gave them the homage of a stereotyped fiction, while following their sexual impulses which conflicted with them. With the publication of the Kinsey Report came the beginning of the end of these deceptions and the growth of widespread public questioning of the social, as well as individual, worth of many of the official sex codes.

As Lester Kirkendall has pointed out, most adults, still looking back to the days of their youth, refuse to recognize that many of the props that have upheld the conventional sexual standards have collapsed and that no new ones have clearly taken their place. The first prop that has dropped away is adult supervision; at the college level it has virtually disappeared. Disapproval by friends or the general community of premarital intercourse is no longer the threat to young college people it used to be, nor does the danger of pregnancy carry with it the same fears. For these reasons, the types of warnings that most parents give their youngsters do not command much attention from older adolescents.

Today, for vast numbers of thoughtful persons many of the old moral absolutes—once thought sacrosanct and not open to any kind of question—are open to serious challenge, not only from persons who want to break the codes for their own pleasure's sake, but more importantly from many who believe that they are actually wrong. Today, for the first time in our history as a nation, the individual is confronted with an array of competing value systems of sex ranging from the rigid, dogmatic, and intolerant philosophy that sees all sex as basically sinful to the latest variation of the current "fun morality." Now, for the first time, the individual is granted a relative amount of freedom to make a personal choice. This is truly an important change.

If our basis of comparison is not just the last generation but the years going back to the Victorian Age, no one will deny the importance of the changes that have taken place with the growing freedom of women. It is a far cry indeed from a time when a leading physician could state publicly (just before the turn of the century) that "any woman who feels pleasure in the sexual relationship is no better than a prostitute" to a time when a report on the sexual responses of men and women observed in intercourse under actual laboratory conditions becomes a nationwide best seller. Since the turn of the century, young men and women have been moving steadily from a formal standard of abstinence before marriage toward a new one of "permissiveness with affection," as Ira Reiss has put it. Certainly a revolution has taken place in patterns of necking and petting as compared with older patterns of "spooning" and "sparking."

Teen-agers are strongly influenced by their desire to conform with the behavior of the teen-age subculture, or at least with the popular image of that subculture. There is a danger that many teen-agers, fed a steady diet of the "sexual revolution," will come to feel that they are in some way unusual if they have not had sexual intercourse. "A large number of boys (25 per cent) and quite a few girls (13 per cent)," said Michael Schofield in his study of young people in Britain, "were driven towards their first experience for reasons that can best be summed up by the word curiosity. Admonitory articles in the press and handwringing by important people have given some adolescents the impression that the average teen-ager is sexually experienced, and some of these boys and girls must have wondered why they were exceptional and whether they were missing something."

Thus, it is important for parents and teachers not to be misled by the many clichés of "the sexual revolution." If they wish to help their youngsters, they must start to look behind the sensational headlines at the real data and begin to face up to the realities of the changing sex behavior in our country.

Part II

What Parents and Teachers
Should Know About
Teen-Age Development

3

Understanding Adolescence

by ISADORE RUBIN, PH.D.

Counselors often tell parents that the best thing they can do, when beset by the unpredictable and seemingly uncontrollable behavior of adolescents, is to comfort themselves with these words, "It will pass. It will pass." Nothing is more important in the guidance of young people than maintaining the sense of perspective that comes from the realization that adolescence is a transitional period in personality development. Like all periods of transition, it presents a number of problems of adjustment and a certain amount of psychological stress.

WHAT IS ADOLESCENCE?

What is adolescence? To begin with, adolescence takes place over a period ranging from about twelve or thirteen to the early twenties, with wide individual and cultural variations. It occurs earlier in girls than in boys. Physically, it is a time when important physiological changes take place, including the maturation of the sexual organs and the appearance of the secondary sex characteristics. Socially, it is a period when the individual must progress from being a dependent child to being a self-sufficient adult. Psychologically, it is a period in which new adjustments have to be made—those which distinguish child behavior from adult behavior. At perhaps no other time in life, except birth, does a transition of such importance take place.

During childhood the boy and girl gain their status from their families and base their attitudes, values, and goals on the frame of reference set up by the family. During adolescence they must begin to achieve their own status and work out their own values and goals. Their problems are multiplied in a period of rapid social change such as they are now living in—the adolescent must not only adjust to his own problems but also to those of a changing society.

THE CENTRAL PROBLEM OF ADOLESCENCE— THE ESTABLISHMENT OF A SENSE OF IDENTITY

Each transitional period in life creates what psychiatrist Erik H. Erikson has called a "crisis in identity." He pointed out that each crisis of transition involves developmental dilemmas, which can be resolved either by moving forward to a new stage or by remaining "frozen" at a level of incomplete development. According to Erikson's theory of personality development, the central problem of adolescence is the establishment of a sense of identity. What the adolescent seeks to clarify is who he is and what his role in society is to be. Is he a child or is he an adult? Does he have it in him to someday be a husband and father? What is he to be as a worker and an earner of money? Can he feel self-confident in spite of the fact that his race or religion or national background makes him a person some people look down upon? Over all, will he be a success or failure?

Important to the person's sense of identity is his self-image and perception of his body. During the normal developmental process, body changes are so slow that the self-image remains relatively stable. It has time to adjust to these changes so that the individual knows his own body. During adolescence, changes in body structure, body experiences, and new body sensations and urges are so drastic that the body image becomes unknown. The adolescent is preoccupied with his body and may be disturbed by it. Any minor blemish or defect causes considerable worry, and few adolescents realize that wide variation is compatible with normality. An important aspect of parent guidance, then, is to make sure the youngster understands this.

In an adverse adult-made world in which they are marginal in varying degrees, adolescents achieve immediate status through conformity to the norms of their age-mate group, or peer groups.

The adolescent peer culture provides a status and social identity for youngsters, plays a major role in facilitating emancipation from the home, transmits social class values, focalizes resistance against adult standards and authority, and serves as the principal training institution of the adolescent period. As adolescents become more and more resistive to adult suggestion, they turn more and more to approval of their peer group, thus resulting in exaggerated emphasis on conformity within the peer group.

Parents should draw an important implication from this. Instead of decrying inevitable group identification, parents should recognize the importance of the peer group and provide supportive guidance so that the group can be used as an element of progress. They must recognize that the group conformity—the adoption of various fads that are often incomprehensible and repugnant to adults—is a self-protective device that arises from the need of the peer culture to maintain its identity as the chief adolescent status-giving institution in our society.

It is commonplace to describe adolescence as a period of rebellion against parental norms and rejection of traditional attitudes and values. However, some authors have challenged the existence of a rebellious young subculture as a "myth." They point out that while rebellion does exist against parents, such conflict occurs *within a value framework* and not characteristically *over* values. According to R. C. Bealer and others:

The adolescent seeking to establish his identity in adult society may disagree with his parents regarding when recognition of his maturity should occur. He may wish to engage in activities which symbolize his adulthood while his parents feel that he is still too young. This type of "rebellion" is as temporary as is the period of adolescence itself, and, rather than rejection of parental norms, it is perhaps better characterized as acceptance of and eagerness to participate in the larger society. . . . This cannot accurately be described as a group rejection of societal norms. It constitutes an individual resistance to specific authority patterns.

Psychiatrist Irene M. Josselyn has noted that if his childhood relationship with his parents was satisfactory, the adolescent, in attempting to achieve a sense of independence, does not rebel against those standards which were instilled in his childhood that are basic to the interliving of our culture. What he does rebel against are those aspects of the parent-child relationship that bind him to childhood.

THE ADOLESCENT OF TODAY

There is a tendency on the part of many parents and even professionals to think of the younger generation as "going to the dogs." These people see in teen-agers a greater tendency to antisocial behavior and promiscuity, disorientation with family and community, and intensified vulnerability to mental breakdown. Others, however, have warned "there are too many unknowns to allow a decision as to whether this generation of adolescents is worse off than adolescents of one, two, three or more generations ago or that the present generation is descending into Hades at all."

Ira Reiss points out that the research evidence available on sexual codes seems at odds with the popular view that teen-agers are irresponsible, promiscuous, and in sharp conflict with adult sexual codes. The venereal-disease rates, unwed-motherhood rates, and studies of teen-age attitudes give evidence of a more conservative pattern than exists for older couples. The real increase in teen-age sexual behavior over the last generation is not in the area of sexual intercourse but in the area of petting and in the public nature of some petting behavior—types of behavior that have been worked out by teen-agers themselves.

Although teen-agers may not be descending to Hades, Jesse Bernard has pointed out that teen-age culture does seem to be moving downward—cosmetics and brassières are now characteristics of younger ages and so is dating. In some places dating may begin as early as ten or eleven.

COUNSELING SUGGESTIONS FOR PARENTS

From these insights come a number of clear counseling suggestions for parents. As youngsters change and grow up, adults' rules, too, must change. Parents must relax their protection and give young people ever-increasing opportunities to do things for themselves. Their real job is to produce an adult, not a child. This is not easy, because parents, and especially mothers, often have a need for dependent children. Many parents grow anxious and unhappy about the adolescent's revolt and growing away from the family. These parents need to be assured that the revolt is an essential preliminary to the business of getting married and founding a new family. Falling out of love with parents is the first step toward falling in love with a mate. The child to be concerned about, psychiatrists say, is the one who remains wholly docile and affectionate during this period.

The role of adults is not to protect adolescents from all adversity and from every difficult experience. It is their obligation to let youngsters do their own experimenting—without freedom to experiment there is no learning of responsibility. Obviously this freedom entails risk. But the only alternative to the risk of freedom is the swaddling cloth of overprotection. But at the same time, it is an adult's role to guide and to give temporary assistance when a young person is faced with overwhelming odds. Youngsters still need discipline and control and can't be left entirely to their own whims and interests. "Until they're ready to ship out alone, they need to feel that the helm is in strong, capable hands."

The ability to make choices among an array of alternatives is an important aspect of growing up in our country. The adolescent is increasingly confronted with conflicting choices in matters of career, personality identity, sexual behavior, and other matters. Since the making of choices in a situation where a lack of definite social canons exist produces anxiety, a special effort must be made by parents to train children and adolescents for the choices they will have to make; they must be given tools whereby they may think and choose.

Although it is more difficult than in other areas, this type of guidance must also be applied in the emotional and taboo-laden area of sex. Realistic sex guidance must equip the boy and girl, not with dogmatic rules that may quickly become meaningless in their lives, but with the ability for intelligent self-determination. To do this, parents must supply precise and reliable information about the advantages and disadvantages, the issues and implications of the various forms of sexual behavior. Answers to questions must be specific and related to the adolescent's actual problems.

One final point is made by David P. Ausubel, a leading authority on adolescence. He suggests that even though reality is unsatisfactory or inconsistent with what the adolescent wishes it might be, youngsters should be encouraged to adjust to current reality and be prepared for the kind of world they are apt to face. This does not imply accepting the status quo, he cautions, but adopting a mature attitude toward social change. In other words, the adolescent should not be given an attitude that leads him to batter his head against the wall of custom. At the same time he should be encouraged to express and courageously defend his moral principles.

4

Signs of Womanhood

by RICHARD STILLER, M.A.

What are the visible signs and symbols that tell us that girlhood is waning and that maturity is just around the corner? Age, of course, should give the watchful parent his first hint. Girls usually start *pubescence*—the first stage of maturation which ends at *puberty*—at about ten or eleven, a year or two earlier than boys. By twelve the first changes of girlhood into womanhood are really quite apparent.

Most obvious is the development of the breasts into small, conical buds. There is also an increase in the size and projection outward of the nipples. Earlier, but perhaps less noticeable, is the gradual widening of the pelvis and the growth of fat pads on the hips. As in boys, the appearance of soft, downy, rather colorless *pubic* hair is the most obvious external evidence of the progress of pubescence.

THE ONSET OF MENSTRUATION

About two years after the breasts begin budding and about one year after the appearance of pubic hair—that is to say, at thirteen, on the average—menstruation first starts. This important development—known as the *menarche*—is the first real indication that the girl is becoming a woman. From this event to the *menopause*— which is the stopping of menstruation (on the average) about thirty-six years later—her womb-lining will slough off each month in the form of menstrual bleeding and then renew itself once more in preparation for a possible pregnancy.

This menstrual bleeding can be quite startling, unless the child has been prepared for it. "Every girl," writes Dr. John F. Oliven, "should have advance notice of what to expect. . . . The instructor (should be) the mother, and age eleven is not too early for this information. Emphasis should be placed on the fact that this is a normal and universal occurrence, and that this is the only instance in human life where bleeding does not signify injury or disease.

"An unprepared girl may fear that she has injured herself internally through petting or masturbating, or that she has a 'disease.' Uninstructed girls have been known to assume that they are giving birth, having an abortion, or bleeding rectally due to cancer."

But we cannot say that menstruation's beginning means *puberty*—the theoretical moment when the girl can first become a mother—has arrived. This will not truly happen until *ovulation*— the releasing of mature eggs by the ovaries—takes place about a year or two after menstruation starts.

Meanwhile, the pubic hair thickens, coarsens, becomes curly, and darkens in color. It develops the distinctive, clearly defined female pattern of an inverted triangle, growing downward into the pubic area. Armpit hair also develops at this time. Finally, at about fourteen or fifteen, the young girl's ovaries will produce their first egg. We can now say that puberty has been reached. From a reproductive viewpoint, she has now, indeed, become a woman, able to conceive and to bear children.

CHANGES IN LATER ADOLESCENT YEARS

Within the next few years, puberty proceeds rapidly. Many girls reach their full stature by about sixteen. By the late teens, the average girl is really more a woman than a "teen-ager." Many important internal or barely visible sexual and reproductive changes quite naturally occur during pubescence and adolescence. The *mons pubis,* the fatty pad just above the *vulva* (the external sex organs), becomes more prominent. The outer lips develop and become fleshier, hiding the rest of the vulva. The vulva is ordinarily quite visible during childhood.

The inner lips also develop, as do the *glands of Bartholin,* just inside the opening of the vagina. These glands, which are assumed to play a part in lubricating the vagina during coitus, now begin to secrete their fluids. The *clitoris* also rapidly develops its extensive system of blood vessels. Some authorities say that at this time it acquires the ability to become erect; others dispute this.

The vagina itself turns a deeper color, and its mucous lining thickens. It will remain thicker until the menopause, when it reverts to the thinness of childhood. The vaginal secretions also now become acid. The womb, starting from age ten, begins to grow. At about twelve this growth becomes quite rapid. By eighteen, at its maximum, it has about doubled in size. Future pregnancy will increase its permanent size slightly.

The ovaries, the female sex glands largely responsible for all these transformations, begin to secrete female sex hormone at age ten. They grow rapidly at the beginning of pubescence, and by the time of first menstruation are about one third of their adult weight. This maximum is usually achieved by about nineteen or twenty.

THE PROBLEMS OF BREAST DEVELOPMENT

Next to the beginning of menstrual bleeding, breast development and breast size are probably the chief sources of worry for many girls and their anxious parents. This is quite natural. After all, the breasts are probably the most visible of all sexual characteristics. In addition, our culture places great stress on the importance and significance of bosom beauty. Some authorities have even criticized what they call our harmful modern "breast obsession," which makes many young girls feel that without exaggerated and prominently displayed breasts they can have no hope of attracting young men and their future husbands.

As we have seen, the breasts first bud at age eleven, about two years before menstruation starts. By puberty, their size and shape is usually at its maximum. Breasts, however, may develop slowly or rapidly. They may even develop unevenly, with one larger than the other during pubescence. By puberty they are usually pretty much the same size. Like all other organs of the body, their normal size is largely hereditary, and cannot really be altered to any great extent.

This, then, is the usual course of development for the average girl. As in all other life processes, there is no rigid timetable which prescribes the exact sequence and date for the appearance of these signs of womanhood. Of one thing we can be sure. Romantic fiction to the contrary, girls will not "suddenly" blossom out into womanhood. If parents are the least bit alert, they can watch and enjoy the steady, unfolding process. It will give them great delight and satisfaction. And if they stay one jump ahead of their daughters they will themselves be prepared for all that may come. And they will be able to help the youngster anticipate and understand the wonderful changes that will turn her from a girl into a young woman.

5

Signs of Manhood

by RICHARD STILLER, M.A.

Serious-minded parents would like to know and to recognize the signs of manhood in their boy. How then can parents tell when boyhood is ending? For one thing, the youngster's age has a lot to do with it. On the average, *pubescence,* which is the stage leading up to *puberty* itself, usually starts for boys at around thirteen and a half years. It is during this period that all the first and sudden changes of beginning manhood will usually be noticed. Girls, of course, start about one to two years earlier.

Puberty itself in boys, generally at age fifteen and a half, is the *end* of this process. Technically, it has not yet arrived until *spermatogenesis*—that is, the production of sperms, or male reproductive cells—has taken place in the *testicle,* or male sex gland. Ejaculation of semen, perhaps as a result of a "wet dream" or of masturbation, occurs anywhere from six months to more than a year earlier.

FIRST SIGN OF PUBESCENCE

The first signs of pubescence that an alert parent will notice are fairly obvious. At about thirteen and a half the boy will suddenly begin to grow in height and weight, and his voice will begin to "break." Of course there will be some definite sexual changes. The scrotum will wrinkle and will grow darker in color; blood vessels will appear and become prominent in its surface. Most obvious will be the soft, downy, rather colorless hair that will make its appearance at the base of the penis.

The appearance of this *pubic* hair has throughout all of history been considered the basic sign of approaching manhood (or womanhood). Actually it is not as reliable an indicator as many believe. Pubic hair grows and changes during this process of maturing. Through puberty and adolescence it becomes darker, coarser, thicker, and curlier. It reaches its mature masculine upward growth toward the navel at about nineteen. Armpit hair follows pubic hair through similar stages at an interval of about six months or more.

"Real" manhood is often measured among boys by its most visible sign: the development of face hair. Perhaps more than any other characteristic of adolescence (with the possible exception of penis size) the growth of the beard has been the "status symbol" of maleness. First appearing on the upper lip, face hair spreads slowly to the chin and the sides of the face. In most cases this does not finally occur until seventeen, at which time perhaps half of all boys shave. Body hair on the chest, etc., appears more slowly, often not until the twenties.

THE GROWTH AND DEVELOPMENT OF THE SEXUAL ORGANS

Of obvious importance is the growth and development of the sex organs, especially the penis. Beginning slowly at eleven, the penis grows rapidly during pubescence, especially after fourteen. By sixteen it has more than doubled its childhood size. It reaches its maximum growth at the end of adolescence. Penis size is a matter of inheritance, just as are other bodily dimensions. Occasionally, as a result of glandular disturbance, the penis does not develop normally. In such cases, treatment by a physician can lead to increased size.

Other sex organs also develop at this time, including the prostate and seminal vesicles. Ejaculation cannot occur until these and related organs are thoroughly matured. The testicles increase markedly in size until their maximum is reached at around seventeen. It is not until these sex glands are able to manufacture sperm—at around fifteen and a half—that puberty can be said to have occurred.

The occurrence of erection, or even of orgasm, is not *necessarily* a sign of puberty. Orgasm—without ejaculation—can occur in children and even infants before pubescence. Erection also is not uncommon in infants and children.

Body growth generally is related closely to this period. A boy will usually grow rapidly in height until about fifteen. Some time between that age and twenty or twenty-one all further growth in height will stop completely. Deepening and widening of the chest, expansion of the shoulders, and development of leg and arm muscles may continue for a little longer.

THE PROBLEM OF EJACULATION

Probably the chief sexual problem for boys at puberty is that concerning ejaculation. This will occur either as a result of masturbation or of a nocturnal emission—a "wet dream." Even if he masturbates, a boy will usually still experience an occasional nocturnal emission. These emissions, are, of course, quite normal. On the average, a boy will have one every two weeks or so, sometimes as often as twice a week. They usually occur during an erotic dream, while the boy is entirely or almost entirely asleep. Occasionally a boy may wake in the morning with a feeling of fatigue or low spirits. Sometimes there is a mild ache or pain in the penis and testicles. All of these unimportant symptoms following emissions are of short duration.

But what is of more concern is the feeling of guilt and shame that boys often develop as a result of this kind of experience. "Every boy," says Dr. John F. Oliven, "should be properly prepared for the impending onset of nocturnal emissions." Pointing out that the father is the best person for this task, he continues: "The father should be advised to stress in his remarks that all boys have these emissions at this age; that they are entirely natural and harmless. . . . The father should be cautioned against making remarks such as, 'It is normal unless it happens too often.' "

A word of caution: do not expect your son to fit into this timetable with any great precision. The ages mentioned here are approximate, as are the rates and schedules of development. Your boy is after all a human being, not a machine.

6

How Boys and Girls Look At Sex

by LESTER A. KIRKENDALL, PH.D.

Boys and girls cannot look at sex in the same way, but they are only dimly aware of this fact. The fact of being male or female means, inevitably, that sex will be seen from different points of view. Nor does this promise to change! So long as men produce only the sperm which begins the entire reproductive process, and so long as women bear the children, these differences will exist.

Physically, women can become victims of a sexual mistake: they can become pregnant. As a result girls are protected and supervised more strictly than boys from a very early age. As a consequence, girls very often resent these restrictions and the fact that boys have greater freedom and more privileges. Some of the bitterness and some of the hard feelings between the sexes which appear later in life arise from just this situation. Generally a boy can have the key to the house, leave and return home without being closely questioned, walk the streets after dark, and set his own hours. *A girl cannot.*

PUBERTY AFFECTS BOYS AND GIRLS DIFFERENTLY

Puberty, or the coming of physical maturity, affects boys and girls differently. Once menstruation begins, the girl faces a monthly event which will influence a number of her activities. Menstruation is a more serious matter for some girls than others, but for all girls it brings an awareness of sex and the significance of the reproductive processes which differs from that of boys. At best, for girls menstruation is something to be attended to; it is probably much of the time a nuisance, and for some even a disturbing or a miserable event.

Boys? Well, they may have nocturnal emissions if they are not masturbating too frequently for this to happen. But these in no way upset their routine. If a boy wants to play football next week, he doesn't have to check his calendar. The need for relating his activities to the functioning of his reproductive system never occurs to him.

INTERCOURSE, PREGNANCY, AND CHILDBIRTH HAVE A DIFFERENT SIGNIFICANCE FOR MEN AND WOMEN

Intercourse for an intelligent girl aware of her own physiology can hardly be entered in the same casual way a boy can enter it. A boy can be almost certain of finding physical pleasure and achieving an orgasm; a girl is less likely to experience this pleasure. If conception should result from casual intercourse, the boy's part is done; the girl's is only begun. Without doubt there are some men who are parents without knowing it; one can be sure this is not true for women.

With pregnancy there are many obvious developments for the girl. She experiences a change in her figure. There is the problem of clothes, the matter of nutrition for the developing child, and the difficulty (in the later stages of pregnancy) in moving about. There may be fear of the physical consequences of giving birth. If the pregnancy is outside marriage, and if the relationship was casual, the woman is almost entirely on her own except as family and friends can, and will, help. Her sexual partner is out of the picture; *he may not even know what is happening.*

Even in marital pregnancy the husband has difficulty in really becoming a vital part of the experience. One evidence of this is the efforts of family life education organizations to help husbands become more nearly partners in the process of pregnancy and childbirth. *There is no choice, however, on the part of the mother. She is a part of it whether she wants to be or not—and there is no getting out of it.*

The same things which have been said about the relation of the male and female to pregnancy can be said with reference to childbirth. It is something the father can participate in only at secondhand. With childbirth comes the production of milk, nursing and caring for the child. This means still another change in figure, and a prolonged period of confinement. With pregnancy, childbirth, and the care of children comes a restriction of movement not experienced by men.

The amount of lifting and carrying which a mother does in caring for a child before he can walk, if computed in foot-pounds of work, would doubtless mount to a surprising figure. In the case of a wanted pregnancy, most women find all this a joy. They are fulfilling a special function in a very different way than a man can. This does not change the point, however. Intercourse, conception, pregnancy, childbirth, and child care are still matters which have a different significance for men and women, and result in their having different feelings and attitudes toward sex.

So the different functioning of the reproductive system produces differences in sexual attitudes and behavior throughout the lives of men and women. If nothing more than physiology was involved, the two sexes would have to look at sex and sexual participation in different ways. *But more is involved.* Around these differences which result from physiology is a network of social practices which further divide the sexes so far as attitudes toward sex are concerned.

THE DOUBLE STANDARD IN AMERICA

One of the most obvious of these ways is the double standard. Under the double standard women have always been more harshly criticized for sexual experimentation and participation than men are. Men are able to take part in casual relationships with little or no criticism. Their activities may be accepted indulgently as "sowing their wild oats." Such behavior on the part of women is much more severely condemned.

These attitudes are changing, however, and it is quite possible that the double standard will gradually disappear. In fact, Ira Reiss in his study *Premarital Sex Standards in America* feels that this is exactly what is happening. Still we can be sure that the biological difference, which can never be erased, will mean that men and women can never look at sexual functioning, the sexual relationship, and the production of children in exactly the same way.

7

Understanding the Male Sex Drive

by LESTER A. KIRKENDALL, PH.D.

THE "BURNING" SEXUAL DESIRES OF ADOLESCENT BOYS

The Apostle Paul used the word "burn" in speaking of sexual desire. When he said, "It is better to marry than to burn," he seemed to suggest that unmarried men were likely to be consumed with a driving, burning sexual passion. Many persons today feel that all adolescent boys are "burning" with sexual desire. They suppose it cannot be otherwise if they are physically normal. Sexual "burning," they think, is a manifestation of the "glands" and their vigorous functioning.

The actual behavior and experiences of young men in their middle and late teens—and here I speak from an experience of over thirty-five years of direct work with them—suggests a different view. Some are "burning." They experience genuine difficulty in containing and directing their sexual desires. Others who are thoroughly healthy and in the best of physical condition do not experience "burning" sexual desires. Their sexual behavior also indicates that they have little difficulty in adjusting to the sexual side of their nature.

I have come to question the accuracy of our ideas about "sex drive," which most people assume is almost entirely physical. Of course, when boys reach maturity, glandular secretions bring about important developments. Body hair appears and voice changes occur. The sex organs reach adult size. The greatly increased physical pleasure which results when the genitals are moved and stimulated is a marked encouragement to sexual activity. The various hormones cause the nerve endings in the sex organs to become much more sensitive. Sexual stimulation is now easy and the pleasurable sensations much keener.

Clearly some relationship exists between the sex glands and sexual behavior. But I believe that the strength of the sex drive is determined very largely by the way an individual thinks and feels toward sex, and therefore it may vary much from time to time in the same individual.

Now it is true that gland secretions do produce a certain amount of body tension and occasionally some restlessness in individuals. For persons who are glandularly normal, however, this is probably not at all a disturbing state—whether it grows into anything bothersome or upsetting depends on the *mental state* of the individual.

In discussing sex problems with teen-age boys and young men, I noted that persons who felt their sex drives were strong and demanding often mentioned feelings of dissatisfaction about themselves and their relationships with others. Frequently they told of unresolved conflicts with members of their families, or of frustration and defeat in the associations with people in general. They might mention problems and failures in school or in their jobs. On the other hand, those individuals who felt that their sex drives were easily managed and caused them little or no difficulty often expressed feelings of satisfaction about themselves and their relations with others. They usually spoke of their family relationships as satisfying. They usually felt, as one of this group put it, "I've had pretty good breaks so far. I'm well satisfied—no complaints to make."

Generally speaking, there were no indications that members of the second group were less endowed with sexual capacity than the first group. There seemed no more reason for saying they were weak in their sexual capacities than there is for saying that the boy who does not engage in racing lacks the capacity to run, and can automatically be judged as slow and cumbersome in his movements.

The expression "the sex drive in the male is strongest during the teen years" seems to imply a physical or biological drive based, as the various writers indicate, on tissue needs or gland functioning. Many persons now feel that all adolescent boys are strongly pushed, one might say "driven," by sexual desire. They also feel, since the drive is biological in nature, that it is very difficult to help adolescent boys to cope with and direct their sexual feelings. Some have taken the attitude that there is little chance of doing more than following a policy of repression—of trying to hold sexual expression to a minimum, and hoping that teen-age boys will keep out of trouble.

A CLARIFICATION OF OUR IDEAS ABOUT THE SEX DRIVE IS NEEDED

If, however, the sex drive is largely a state of mind, as I believe it is, an entirely different approach to teen-age boys is needed—one that will emphasize the creation of proper attitudes to sex. What is needed is the awareness that when we speak about "drive" we are probably talking about several different things. "Sex drive" has become a catch-all phrase that confuses the elements with which we are actually dealing. We must distinguish between sexual capacity, sexual performance, and sexual drive or desire. We also need a clearer idea of the extent to which the *drive for expression through sex* (this is the way the phrase should be worded) is the result of physical conditions, and the extent to which it arises from the individual's psychological state or from social conditions.

The term "drive" as ordinarily used seems to imply a drive that is primarily physiological in origin. The truth probably is that it is a combination of both physiological and psychological factors, with the psychological factors most decisive in determining the form and extent of sexual behavior. Clarification of our ideas about sex drive would lead to a better approach to sex education of young people. It would be recognized that attitudes and insights, rather than physiology, are crucial to sexual behavior, and stress would be placed there rather than on physiological facts and reproductive information.

Part I I I

What Young People Really Want to Know About Sex

8

Teen-Age Sex Questions

by DERYCK D. CALDERWOOD

Everyone is aware of the obvious difference between males and females in their early teens. One difference that even parents and teachers might not know about, however, is the sharp difference in the sex questions asked by boys and those asked by girls. For the past five years this author has conducted sex-education courses for adolescent boys and girls in the eighth through the twelfth grades. In these courses, the teen-agers were encouraged to write down the sex questions that troubled them most. Since they were not asked to write their names, the questions were completely frank.

QUESTIONS ASKED BY BOYS

Boys usually think they know all about sex. Their idea of manliness makes it extremely hard for them to admit any lack in their sex information. They feel a sense of relief and a real eagerness to learn, however, when they are provided with an opportunity to get correct information without losing face. Boys also have more need than girls for reliable sex information from sources outside the home. They do not have the same natural opportunity for facing sex matters with parents such as the start of menstrual bleeding makes possible for girls. Problems such as nocturnal emissions, sex organ size, and masturbation are usually avoided or overlooked by parents. Embarrassment on the boy's part makes the efforts of parents who do attempt to discuss matters very difficult.

Boys, with their natural drive for independence, often prefer to acquire this information on their own rather than accept parental advice or information. Sometimes they don't even know the right word to use. One ninth grade boy stated, "I wouldn't trust myself to ask most adults about sex. If I slipped and used a dirty word, they'd drop dead from shock."

The questions asked by boys most frequently concerned the male sex organs, masturbation, and homosexual behavior. Intercourse, venereal disease, the meaning of certain slang terms, female sex organs, prostitution, and birth followed in that order. Miscellaneous questions concerned nudism, "dirty" pictures, incest, and parental attitudes toward sex.

Sample questions concerning the male sex organs were: (1) "Why do I have erections so much?" (2) "Why are some of the guys circumcised?" (3) "What way should your penis curve?" (4) "Why do some of us just have one testicle?" (5) "What's the world record measurement for a penis?" These questions can be pretty well summed up by the most frequently asked question: (6) "How can I tell if my sex organs are normal?" (*Answers to the above and to following questions will be found at the end of the chapter. Editors.*)

Information about the considerable difference in the rate of growth among different individuals is helpful to boys. It is also reassuring to emphasize the relative unimportance of genital size in achieving satisfactory sexual intercourse.

Typical questions about masturbation were: (7) "How often can you masturbate?" (8) "Can playing with yourself stop you from having children later?" (9) "Will my penis get too developed if I do it too much?" (10) "Why do they say masturbating doesn't hurt you but tell you not to do it anyhow?" These questions reveal that misinformation and rumor are still the rule rather than the exception on this subject and that it is constantly necessary to reassure youngsters that masturbation will not hurt them in any way or prevent them from having children later. While boys might ask their parents or teachers about other sex matters, masturbation is so personal and shameful to them that it is difficult for them to approach an adult for help since to do so would be taken as an admission of guilt.

Questions on homosexual behavior include: (11) "What is sodomy?" (12) "How can you tell if a person is a homo?" (13)

"Can you get cured if you are a homosexual?" (14) "How can you handle queers?" As with the subject of masturbation, discussion of homosexuality remains taboo in most situations. Some understanding of homosexuality and information on how to handle approaches made by adult homosexuals is vitally important. Many boys have had some homosexual contacts before leaving junior high school. An explanation of the difference between occasional youthful exploratory sex play with other boys and fixed homosexual behavior as an adult could prevent a good deal of guilt and worry.

Any uncertainty about his physical development, or confusion about masturbation, increases a boy's worry and fear of homosexuality. Boys are quick to interpret smaller sex organs, any slight indication of femininity in manner, or lack of ability in sports, as possible indications of homosexuality in themselves and others. This is, of course, completely wrong.

The boys' questions about intercourse showed about half wanted to learn about the total experience, or as one boy expressed it, "more than that old line that it is the act of placing the penis in the vagina." The other half revealed a personal worry about whether they would be able to perform the sex act adequately. Teen-agers are also concerned about the statistics on premarital intercourse, and want to know whether it is "right or wrong."

The questions about venereal disease are usually divided between those who have heard nothing more than the names of the diseases and want more complete information and others who have questions about the possibility of getting a venereal disease from toilet seats, drinking fountains, or from using someone else's towel or athletic supporter. It is reassuring to most boys to know that it is only through close physical contact such as kissing or intercourse that the venereal diseases are spread. Boys feel that information about syphilis and gonorrhea should be taught in their schools.

QUESTIONS ASKED BY GIRLS

Girls take the "facts of life" matter-of-factly. They have been aware of them earlier, in keeping with their earlier entrance into puberty. Their ability to talk to parents is much more advanced and they find discussing sex with mother is fairly easy. While they are aware of the physical changes in themselves, they are less apt to be aware of emotional ones. Their own moods and reactions often leave them confused. Girls have fewer unanswered questions at this age, and in strong contrast to the boys have no questions concerning their own sex organs. Few of them worry about masturbation, and only rarely do they ask the meaning of slang terms. *Their questions about intercourse are largely related to the process of birth and birth control.*

The one area where girls have many questions is the matter of boys. Most boys actually know more about the female body than they do about their own physical development. Girls are quite different. Boys can name the female organs, describe their function, and have generally accurate information about menstruation. As a tenth-grade boy explained it, "All we talk about is girls. Guys are afraid they'll be labeled 'queer' if they talk about their own body to another boy." Girls, through talking with their mothers, have a fairly clear picture of their own body and its functions, but few know anything about boys' nocturnal emissions, erections, or male masturbation.

More than half of the questions from girls usually begin, "What does a *boy* think about . . . ?" While boys are still struggling to understand themselves, the girls are already involved in trying to understand and get along with the opposite sex: (15) "What does a boy think about form-fitting dresses?" (16) "What does a boy think about the way a girl sits or walks?" (17) "Do boys have the same mixed up and embarrassed feelings that girls do?" (18) "What do boys want a girl to let them do?"

Girls' questions also indicate their general attitude toward males to be one of handling or managing them. Much thought is given as to how to get a boy to ask for a date, how to manage the circumstances so that the boy will be required to act in a certain manner, or (through teaming up with Mother) how to "handle" Dad in a difficult situation.

In their questions about venereal disease the girls again demonstrated a sharp difference. Their interest centered around the relationship of the couple rather than the physical facts: (19) "What are the reasons people would have for intercourse if they might get a disease from it?" (20) "How could you ever tell your parents if you got VD?"

Typical miscellaneous questions from girls were: (21) "Why don't they have dirty magazines for girls like they do for boys?" (22) "Can a girl have a baby by her father?" (23) "Is a prostitute a girl who pays a man to have intercourse with her?" and (24) "If parents really understand our teen-age problems, why can't they let us know more so we'll feel at ease?"

Boys and girls are in unanimous agreement about the value of sex education that deals with their questions frankly. They appreciate guidance that is aimed at directing them toward mutual trust in their relations with each other. These certainly seem more and more important in a time when boy-girl relationships are beginning at increasingly earlier ages.

ANSWERS TO THE ABOVE QUESTIONS

(1) It is natural for teen-age boys to have frequent erections. (2) Some boys are circumcised for religious reasons—because they are Jewish—and others because some doctors automatically circumcise all boy babies in the belief that this is a hygienic practice. (3) A slight curvature either to the left or the right is quite normal. (4) A small percentage of boys have one undescended testicle which remains in the abdomen or in the canal between the abdomen and the scrotum. (5) The longest penis on record is 14 inches, erect, while average size is 5 to 6 inches. (6) By physical examination by a doctor. (7) It depends on the individual. (8) No. (9) No. (10) Because most adults attach feelings of guilt and shame to sex, and especially to masturbation.

(11) It usually refers to anal intercourse. (12) You usually can't unless he openly attempts sex relations with another male. (13) Yes, in many cases, if you really want to. (14) The same way you should "handle" anyone else, firmly but without hostility or panic. (15) He finds them sexually exciting. (16) He often thinks she is being deliberately sexy, especially if her position is sexually exciting. (17) Yes. (18) They want girls to let them go as far as possible in necking, petting, and other sexual acts. (19)

The sex drive is stronger—especially at the moment—than fear of disease.

(20) You would have to have an excellent and trusting relationship with one or both of your parents. But even if you did not, you should still see a doctor about it. (21) Because girls—unlike boys—are not usually sexually stimulated by what they see or read. (22) Yes. (23) No. A prostitute is a girl who is paid by men who have intercourse with her. (24) Because parents usually find it very difficult to overcome their own feelings of guilt and shame about sex, and in addition they are afraid to give their children correct sex information because they fear (mistakenly) that this will encourage them to become sexually promiscuous.

9

Questions Girls Ask About Menstruation

by JEROME S. MENAKER, M.D.

The following questions are commonly put to gynecologists by young girls or by their mothers. Many girls who do not voice the questions do have them or feel some concern about many of these problems. Parents and teachers should find proper occasions to see that these questions are answered.

Why does menstruation occur?

Menstruation occurs because the body prepares food for a possible guest. When the guest does not appear to partake of that food, the body discards it and starts anew the next month. Once the menstrual cycle is established, the womb (uterus) builds up a thick velvety lining, rich in blood, to nourish and nest a fertilized egg which will go on to develop into a baby. If the egg remains unfertilized it disintegrates and is dissolved in the body. The uterus no longer has any need for the prepared food, which will not keep "fresh" from one month to the next; so it discards this lining in the form of menstrual blood and in the new cycle prepares a fresh meal for the expected guest, the fertilized egg. If a fertilized egg does present itself, the proper food for its earliest growth is ready so that development can continue. When this happens, menstruation does not occur.

Why do some girls start menstruating at the age of eleven and others not until several years later?

For the same reason that some girls start to walk, talk, develop teeth, and grow tall at different times from their sisters or friends. The "master gland" of the body which controls growth, development and menstruation is the pituitary gland. This may bring about maturity in the menstrual apparatus at any age from ten to seventeen years with an average, in this country, of about thirteen years. Only if signs of general maturity, breast development, fullness of figure, axillary (armpit) and pubic hair, etc., occur before the age of ten or after sixteen-seventeen should one consult a physician. *Remember, "normal" for bodily functions is always a range and never a single figure.*

How long should a period normally last?

Here again the norm is a range. The average is three to five days. Two to seven days are certainly normal.

What is the total amount of blood that is lost, on the average?

The average loss is an ounce and a half or three tablespoonsful, with a normal range of from one to five ounces.

Are blood clots abnormal?

Ordinarily menstrual blood does not clot so that clotting usually means a fairly heavy flow. Small bean-sized clots usually should cause no alarm but clots larger around than a nickel usually indicate the need for a visit to the doctor.

If the menstrual period comes early or is delayed at any time (under circumstances where pregnancy is not possible), does that mean that anything is wrong?

No, not at all. Many, many things may influence the menstrual cycle, making it either early or late. Among these things are sorrow, such as illness of a parent; joy, such as an approaching marriage; a cold, chilling, or even an airplane trip.

If periods are irregular and menstrual flow varies, should a physician be consulted even if there seems to be nothing wrong?

Yes, if periods are totally irregular or widely varied in amount of flow, it would be wise to consult a physician.

How does one figure the length of the menstrual cycle?

One counts the period from the first day of flow of one period to the first day of the next. It is also good to record the number of days of flow and the average number of pads used per day.

What conditions in a young girl require medical attention?

Excessive cramping, especially that which requires a girl to go to bed, a flow so excessive that doubled pads are required, extreme irregularity or undue irritability and nervousness before a period—all these are conditions that should be brought to a physician.

Is it normal to have pain before or during menses?

It is normal—but by no means necessary—to have a few cramps or moderate discomfort. If more than a few aspirins or a heating pad are required, a physician should be consulted.

What causes cramps and what can be done for them?

This is a question that even gynecologists and physiologists cannot agree upon, so it would be idle to present the pros and cons of the various arguments here. Suffice it to say that if cramps are so severe that the simple measures already described do not bring relief, a doctor should be consulted. Not all cramps are caused by the same thing, but in almost every instance a combination of exercise and medication can be prescribed that will bring the desired relief.

Why is a girl more emotional during a menstrual period?

Because there may be an imbalance in the body hormones that control menstruation. Such an imbalance leads to varying degrees of emotional upset during and more especially before a period. Help from a physician is readily available which can prevent and relieve such emotional upsets.

Is it wise to take only baths, not showers, during the period? What precautions have to be observed? How about swimming?

Either baths or showers are permissible, in fact recommended daily during a period. The precautions are simply the ones that common sense would dictate, i.e., don't take them too hot or too cold, and avoid chilling after a bath or shower. Swimming is permissible during any except the days of heaviest flow. Here again one should avoid chilling or excessive fatigue.

Is exercise all right during menstruation?

Yes indeed, moderate daily exercise that a girl is already used to is not only all right, but beneficial.

How about strenuous physical work?

Unless flow is very moderate and one is ordinarily used to daily strenuous work, such work is best avoided or done in moderation during the period.

How can odors during the menstrual period be prevented?

By daily bathing and normal attention to personal hygiene and grooming. All modern pads and tampons for sale include a mild deodorant.

Does menstruation cause a girl's face to break out in pimples? If so, why?

Usually not, but menstruation may cause the face to break out in, or more especially aggravate, an already pre-existing condition.

The reason lies in an imbalance in hormones, those body chemical regulators that control menstruation. Here once again good medical advice can do a great deal to prevent or alleviate the pimples.

Is it all right for a virgin to use tampons?

This is not fairly a "yes" or "no" question, since doctors may disagree on the answer to this one. My own opinion is that many virgins can wear a vaginal tampon with complete safety, efficiency, and great satisfaction.

If periods are irregular, how can a girl be prepared for menstruation?

By carrying several pads or tampons in her purse at all times.

Does one menstruate if one or both ovaries are removed?

If just one ovary is removed, the menstrual cycle will probably be re-established monthly just as it was before. If both ovaries are removed, menstruation ceases.

Can boys tell when girls are menstruating?

No! A boy cannot tell when a girl is menstruating from anything in her physical appearance.

Can you take anything to delay menstruation (because of vacation, honeymoon, athletic meets, etc.)?

Yes, there are new oral hormone preparations that can do this, but it is tricky business to be done only under supervision of a physician.

Until what age do women menstruate?

The range is even wider here than the range in ages at which menstruation commences. About forty-eight to fifty are average, but an occasional normal woman may menstruate until age sixty.

10

Sex Worries of Teen-Age Boys

by LESTER A. KIRKENDALL, PH.D.

If you have an adolescent boy in your home, or if you know one, you can be pretty sure that there are a number of questions about sex which he would like to have answered. You can also be sure that these questions are ignored in the occasional school programs in sex education as too touchy and delicate to handle. It is still more likely that those who handle such instruction are unaware that these worries and concerns even exist, for they are certainly seldom mentioned by the adolescent.

Many boys are concerned about some features of sexual development or functioning. "Why do I have an erection when I wake up in the morning?" "Is my penis the right size?" Others worry needlessly about some kind of sexual conduct. "What are the consequences of masturbation?" "I have been involved in sex play with a boy friend. What should I do?" Many wonder whether they will know what to do in future intercourse or whether they will be able to satisfy their wives. Some are disturbed by thoughts or dreams about sex or by unexpected erections. They are afraid that such occurrences mean that they are oversexed or immoral.

CONCERN ABOUT SLOW GENITAL DEVELOPMENT

A boy who is worried about slow genital development may find some comfort in knowing that this is not really a sexual problem. It is simply a part of the physical pattern which belongs to him. An explanation of individual differences may be helpful at this point. Just as there are some who mature late, there are those who mature early. Then, too, there are tall and short persons, fast and slow runners, people who gain weight easily and those who do not. Each pattern has its advantages and its drawbacks.

Perhaps the coach or physical education teacher can help. A clear explanation in class of variation in patterns and rates of human development, and the importance of each person respecting the pattern of the other fellow should be given. This may save the undeveloped boy the "kidding" or razzing remarks which he may receive. Personal conferences with those who hurt by kidding may be necessary. But once they appreciate how the immature boy feels there is usually sympathy rather than tormenting.

Late development is also sometimes a family characteristic. The late-maturing child may be helped by knowing that other members of the family have had a similar experience. This can be especially helpful if the boy admires Uncle John. Suppose Uncle John was a late-maturing individual, but is now fully developed and satisfied with himself just like anybody else. The boy may identify with him to the point that his concern becomes much less pressing. The boy's concern about the size of genital organs should be frankly acknowledged. Once the parents speak frankly about his uneasiness it is much easier to handle. In fact such concerns as a deep worry over genital size are arrived at by a process of brooding, isolation, and cover-up.

So far as size of the genitals is concerned, the boy should know that penile size has little or no significance either in determining sexual adjustment or in indicating masculinity. Ideas that organ size is important in coitus have no foundation in fact. Neither can one judge the size of an erect penis from observation of the size of the flaccid organ. Boys often observe each other in showers or when dressing, and reach unwarranted conclusions about genital size. Some boys may experience much more of an enlargement in attaining an erection than others. Even this may differ somewhat from time to time in the same individual.

Parents or counselors who talk about such a concern need to draw a nice line between talking about it enough that the boy's concerns are removed (and this usually means more than once) and harping on it. If the adult keeps returning to the subject this may indicate disturbance to the boy even though the parent means to be reassuring. It is probably enough to ask once or twice after the first discussion if the boy feels all right about the matter. If he does, then let the subject drop.

Sometimes, it should be pointed out, underdevelopment does indicate a physical condition which needs the attention of a doctor. Some glandular condition may be causing difficulty and be in need of correction. This glandular condition is characterized not only by small genitals, but by small or undescended testicles, marked fat deposits on hips, buttocks, belly and chest, weak muscle development and various other traits. In all cases, especially when late maturation is not a family characteristic, it would be well to have this condition checked on by a physician. He should be in a position to help parents know if there is a cause for genuine concern.

OTHER CONCERNS ABOUT GENITAL ANATOMY

Some boys are worried about other features of their genital anatomy, which because of the lack of information assume frightening aspects. Thus a boy may worry because one testicle hangs lower than the other, or because he can feel protuberances on the testicle, over the prominence of veins as they stand out on the penis and/or the testicles. He may feel that a sticky, colorless discharge at the tip of the penis denotes a disease. *Actually, all of these are perfectly normal features of development.*

Boys who are worried about genital curvature are relieved to find there is no evidence that this interferes with sexual functioning or performance. Kinsey's data indicates that a definite up-curvature is found in 15 to 20 per cent of all individuals. While I know of no other authentic information concerning the frequency of curvature, I have come across it frequently enough in my study of worries to convince me that upward curvature, or some deflection to the right or left, is fairly common.

A few boys feel concern over a soreness and slight swelling around the nipples which they experience about the time they enter puberty. This is due to an overactivation by hormonal secretions of the glands around the nipple, and it usually lasts for just a short time. This brief period may produce some real mental anguish, however.

CONCERNS ABOUT ERECTIONS

One of the most common concerns is with morning erections, i.e., erections present upon awaking. Although this seems to be a universal male experience, it is not understood by many young adolescents. Many boys are "embarrassed," or "guilty," or fearful that morning erections indicate an abnormal sex desire. One boy asked if morning erections could mean that one might become a "sex maniac." Most boys have observed that, upon voiding the bladder, the erection disappears, and so they attribute the erection to a distended bladder. This is apparently only a part of the explanation, for an equally full bladder during waking hours does not ordinarily produce an erection.

The most plausible explanation is that during the hours just before waking, when sleep is fitful, a certain amount of erotic material flits through the uncensored mind. The likelihood of this happening may be increased by the pressure which a distended bladder exerts on the nerve endings in the area around the genitals. Whatever the correct explanation, for there may be others, there certainly is no reason for a boy to fear that morning erections are abnormal or shameful. Nor do morning erections, or the sex dreams which accompany them, indicate that he has dangerous sexual tendencies.

Some boys are troubled by the rapidity with which they attain erection through exposure to almost any sexual stimulus. When on dates with girls, some boys find themselves with an erection when some girl no more than comes into physical contact with them. She may brush by the boy or their hands come into contact. A kiss may be a tremendous stimulant, and even the sight of certain girls, especially when their dress is revealing, may cause erections. Some boys are mystified, troubled, or guilt-ridden over these reactions, and when given an opportunity express their concern over them.

Another kind of experience with erections troubles boys in a different way. Most boys—especially those between the ages of thirteen and sixteen—complain that they have erections unexpectedly and in situations which embarrass and distress them. Some have mentioned noticing erections while taking an examination, while sitting at a desk studying, in a waiting room, or while watching exciting movies. Kinsey in *Sexual Behavior in the Human Male* lists sixty-four nonsexual sources of erotic stimulation reported by younger boys, so the fact of genital responses to nonsexual stimuli seems well established.

It appears to me that many boys at the age of puberty possess a nervous system which has been made highly sensitive and quickly responsive to stimuli of various kinds, sexual and nonsexual. These stimuli are experienced in the form of sexual excitement, fears, general excitements, emotional upsets, and frustrations that produce strains and tensions in the body. The newly activated nervous system responds, but fails, because neural pathways are not yet well established to do a good job of directing particular stimuli to the organs which would ordinarily be expected to respond to them. As a result we have adolescent boys who respond, helter-skelter, hit-and-miss, with erections to all kinds of stimuli. As further evidence that the adolescent nervous system has trouble differentiating responses, we occasionally see adolescents who cry when no one expects them to, or who hit someone when they might be expected to run.

The biggest assistance parents and teachers could give the boy would be to help him understand what is happening to his body, and how normal it is. Above all they should help him feel these changes are acceptable to others and so he can accept them, too. A serious mistake is made when a boy tries to handle these impulses by denying he has them and by fighting them. This only increases the tensions and makes the original problem worse.

I have had most success in helping boys by getting them to realize that these unexpected erections were simply an aspect of normal living. If they happened, they happened and no one was better or worse for it. These physical experiences need present no difficulty if one can but understand and accept them for what they are—normal physical reactions. Once the individual has been able to do this he is able to direct his thinking toward constructive social adjustment. And interestingly enough, because he is no longer tense and worried, the troublesome erections begin to disappear also.

11

College Students' Sex Questions

by DONALD N. BOYDSTON, M.S., ED.D.

For the last decade this writer, while teaching in two different state universities, has been studying questions about personal sex problems turned in by students in health education classes. These questions have been used to develop teaching units in social hygiene for college students. The questions were submitted anonymously with the students identifying themselves only by age and sex. Because the students realized they could not be embarrassed by their own queries, since not even the teacher would be aware of their identity, some extremely revealing questions were turned in over the ten-year period.

THE TYPES OF QUESTIONS ASKED
AND WHAT THEY INDICATE

If, as most modern educators agree, questions are an excellent indication of the needs of our teen-agers, then it seems fairly certain that our college students, who should be among the best informed and intelligent in our society, are woefully lacking in information about themselves and their sexual problems. Recently twenty-two hundred of these questions were analyzed. A table showing the number of questions and their percentage in each category can be found on page 73.

Studying the questions, it seems fairly obvious that the average college student, male or female, wants the answer to three burning questions: (1) What are the best birth-control methods? (2) How far should young couples go in petting? (3) What percentage of college students have sexual intercourse and with what frequency? There are other questions that recur rather frequently also, but the above three are repeated over and over by students in one form or another.

If we were to believe some present-day researchers, perhaps half of our college women have had sexual intercourse. However, a much higher percentage of college women are asking such questions as: "What are the harmful effects of intercourse during menstruation?" "Can your husband tell whether or not you are a virgin?" and "Does sexual experience before marriage have anything to do with happiness in marriage?"

Questions turned in by students show a range from almost abject ignorance to advanced sophistication. Old wives' tales and other superstitions are obviously believed by many. Here are several questions that were turned in during the past calendar year: "Is it true that during menstruation, when one washes her hair or bathes in a tub, it will affect childbirth later?" This question came from a nineteen-year-old coed who obviously had been the victim of poor sexual teaching and and who, we can assume, probably has other strange sex ideas.

Two questions from a married female student show that even college students have developed some rather strict taboos about sexual activity between male and female and may feel that such activity should be confined to a single prescribed type of behavior. Her questions were: "If man and wife tend to enjoy acts of homosexuality with each other, how is that looked upon by others?" "If male and female have practiced acts of homosexuality on each other, does this mean that their children may be homosexual?"

Obviously the students asking these questions do not realize there is no such thing as abnormal or "homosexual" acts between husband and wife as long as both accept activities as a part of love play and have no reservations at the time or later guilt feelings about what they have done. This point is a delicate one that is sometimes rather difficult to make with college students.

Questions About Sex in Marriage

The lack of understanding about the role sex should play in marriage is often revealed by the younger and more inexperienced coeds. One seventeen-year-old freshman coed wanted to know if sexual intercourse was necessary for a successful marriage. Another student asked: "Are there some marriages where the man and wife have decided that they do not want sex except in those instances where they wish to have children" and "If I know that I am frigid and never wish to have sex, does that mean that I should never marry, or are there men who feel as I do?"

Questions About Masturbation

Questions about masturbation show that the extent of ignorance among college students about this activity is great. The following questions are fairly common: "Does masturbation cause sterility?" "Does it cause insanity?" "Does it cause body odor and pimples?" "Does it make you unfit for marriage?"

Other questions about masturbation show that some of the experts in the field of sex education and social hygiene have made an impression. Such questions as the following show more knowledge about the subject: "Some books say that musturbation is common among teen-agers. If I am nineteen years old and have never masturbated, am I frigid or lacking in sex drive?" This query came from a coed who obviously was striving to better understand herself and her basic drives or lack of them.

Another question from at least a partially informed nineteen-year-old male student was: "I have read in several books and magazines that masturbation is not harmful. However, I believe I have indulged too much. Isn't it possible that excessive masturbation can cause physical weakness?"

Without doubt, college students—just like most individuals—need to be given the information and knowledge we have concerning masturbation.

What College Sudents Ask About Sex

Category	No. of Questions	Percentage
1. Birth control	499	22.68
2. Premarital sexual intercourse	202	9.18
3. Marriage	201	9.13
4. Petting	180	8.18
5. Intercourse and health	134	6.09
6. Pregnancy	119	5.40
7. Sex education	105	4.77
8. Masturbation	93	4.22
9. Sexual adjustment	71	3.22
10. Sex drive	68	3.09
11. Menstruation	68	3.09
12. Sex perversion	48	2.18
13. Heredity	41	1.86
14. Orgasm	39	1.77
15. Controlling the sex drive	29	1.31
16. Homosexuality	27	1.22
17. Venereal disease	27	1.22
18. Abortion	25	1.13
19. Normal frequency (of intercourse)	23	1.04
20. Frigidity	21	.95
21. Genitalia	19	.86
22. Sex techniques	17	.77
23. Intercourse during menstruation	13	.59
24. Virginity	11	.50
25. Causes of divorce (sexual)	10	.45
26. Artificial insemination	8	.36
27. Alcohol and sex	8	.36
28. Sex dreams	8	.36
29. Sex and love	8	.36
30. Sterility	7	.31
Total	2,129	

In addition, there were 71 questions dealing with miscellaneous problems, making a total of 2,200.

Questions About Female Frigidity

Another category of questions which may not be as large as some previously cited but which appears consistently year after year deals with female frigidity. Many coeds have evidently examined themselves critically in regard to their sex drive and have become concerned about their lack of interest in sex. They ask many such questions as: "If you are frigid when you are eighteen does this mean that you will always be frigid?" "Is it true that most girls are frigid until the right man comes along?" "Why are boys so much more interested in sex than girls, and does this mean that most girls are cold about sex?"

And from students whose viewpoints are almost opposite come such questions as: "Is it possible for a girl to have strong natural sex drives and still be a virgin?" and "If Kinsey feels that sexual intercourse before marriage is a good preparation for marriage, then why do girls have to act cold and frigid about such an experience?" As perhaps might be suspected, the last question came from a twenty-one-year-old male who was misquoting Kinsey and perhaps had his own personal campaign to change some of the basic attitudes of coeds he knew.

Questions About Petting

One of the leading categories of inquiry, that concerning petting, produced questions that were often somewhat hard to interpret. The reason for this generally can be found in the various definitions that college students have for petting. Some consider petting to be any type of physical contact that may include no more than handholding and kissing. Others interpret petting to mean the closest type of physical contact, with orgasms often being realized by one or both partners by manual or other means.

The various types and definitions of petting make it extremely difficult to talk objectively about petting as a phenomenon of dating or courtship. Some of the questions concerning petting serve to show the wide variation in the definitions of this activity: "In petting, is 'French' kissing considered immoral?" "In petting, since most college students do it to some extent, where do you draw the line anatomically? At the neck, at the waist, or are there limits?" "If in petting the couple engage in homosexual acts, will this affect them in a later marriage?" "What are some of the physical dangers of petting? Effects on the boy?" "Can the act of petting sometimes cause pregnancy by the transfer of sperm cells from the male's hands to the female vagina, or can pregnancy be caused by close body relationships between a boy and girl without having had actual intercourse?"

Questions such as the above would seem to indicate that college students run the gamut of possible petting techniques that can be employed. If we are to believe research, petting among college students is quite different than for those of lower educational levels.

Kinsey states that "Such petting as does occur in the grade school group [i.e., those persons with only grade-school education] is often incidental, confined to a few minutes of hugging and kissing prior to actual coitus, and quite without the elaborations which are usual among college students. Petting at the upper levels may be indefinitely prolonged, even into hours of intensive erotic play, and usually never arrives at coitus. Orgasm as a product of petting occurs among 16 per cent of the males of the grade school level, 32 per cent of the males of the high school level, and over 61 per cent of the college-bred males who are not married by the age of 30."

In other words, a good percentage of college students do engage in petting that is usually prolonged, involved, and which in most cases results in orgasm. For these reasons, questions from college students about petting are often involved and complex. In order to help solve individual problems, it is often necessary to consult with the student on an individual basis.

Questions About Abortion

Closely related to the questions about sexual intercourse are the queries about conception, childbirth, and abortion. Although questions about abortion constituted only about 1 per cent of those submitted, the tone of question received often indicated the fact that the person asking the question had had or currently had some personal involvement in such a problem. The most common questions we are asked about abortion deal with whether the person having an abortion then becomes sterile. Not many ask about the possibilities of death from an abortion, but the following questions reappear fairly often: "Is abortion legal anywhere in this country?" "Will a person who has had an abortion be more apt to develop cancer of the uterus in later years?" "What percentage of women have an abortion in their lifetimes?"

This chapter has given only a sampling of the many questions college students ask. By the very nature of the questions we can see that many college students are confused and concerned about their sexual problems.

Part IV

What Teen-Agers
Should Know About
Anatomy and Reproduction

12

A Glossary of Sexual and Anatomical Terms Young People Should Know

by ISADORE RUBIN, PH.D.

CLITORIS. The clitoris, the center of sexual sensation in girls and women, plays an important part in foreplay and in the achievement of orgasm. It is a small mound of tissue located just above the urethra where the inner lips come together. About the size of a pea, it retracts when sexual arousal takes place. It is somewhat similar in structure to the male penis.

EJACULATION. The expulsion of male semen at the climax of the sexual act. There is no ejaculation in the female.

ERECTION. The stiffening and enlargement of the penis as a result of sexual excitement. Erection, which is brought about by an increased flow of blood into the penis, makes it possible to insert the penis into the female vagina.

EROGENOUS ZONES. The parts of the body that are specially sensitive sexually when they are touched or stroked. These vary in intensity of response and in importance in different persons.

FALLOPIAN TUBES. The narrow tubes that extend from the uterus out to the ovaries and through which the egg generally passes.

FOREPLAY. The stages of petting preliminary to intercourse, in which the partners stimulate each other by kissing, touching, and caressing.

FRIGIDITY. Coldness, indifference, or insensitivity on the part of the female to sexual intercourse or sexual arousal. The main cause is psychological or emotional.

GONADS. The sex glands—ovaries in the female and testes in the male.

HYMEN. The thin membrane partly covering the entrance of the vagina in most but not all females who have not had intercourse. It is usually torn during first intercourse.

IMPOTENCE. The inability of the male to achieve and maintain erection sufficient for intercourse. In young men, it is almost always caused by some kind of fear or anxiety. Temporary impotence can be the result of worry or fatigue.

LABIA, OR LIPS. The large outer lips and the small inner lips surrounding the vagina and other external female sex organs; they are extremely sensitive sexually.

ORGASM. The peak or climax of sexual activity, followed by explosive physical spasms and convulsions, and by ejaculation in the male.

OVARY. The female sex gland that produces eggs (ova) as well as sex hormones. The egg, when fertilized by a male cell, develops into a new being.

OVULATION. The process by which an egg is released from the ovary, usually at about the midpoint in the monthly menstrual cycle.

PENIS. The male sex organ that becomes erect when arousal takes place.

SCROTUM. The bag of skin and muscle, containing the testicles, that hangs between the thighs just below the penis.

SEMEN. The yellowish-white, sticky fluid ejaculated from the penis at orgasm, containing sperm cells (in the fertile male) and fluids manufactured in different glands.

SEX HORMONES. Chemical substances produced by the sex glands and sent into the bloodstream to stimulate various parts of the body.

SEXUAL FANTASY. A thought picture that may occupy a person's mind while he is experiencing erotic or sexual feelings. Often, in the male, these may be pictures of an attractive movie star or "pin-up" girl.

SEXUAL INTERCOURSE. The sexual act in which the male penis is inserted into the female vagina and moved back and forth until orgasm occurs.

SPERM. The male cell, manufactured in the testes, that combines with the female egg to produce new life.

SPERM DUCTS. The tubes or ducts, technically known as *vasa deferentia* (*vas deferens,* singular), that convey the sperm to the point where they are ejaculated.

TESTES. The male sex glands, or gonads, that produce sperm as well as male sex hormones; also known as testicles.

UTERUS. The womb of the female, in which the unborn child develops for a period of nine months.

VAGINA. The female sex organ, by means of which sexual intercourse takes place. It is also the "birth canal" through which the newborn infant emerges.

VULVA. The sensitive external sex organs of the female, consisting of the outer and inner lips (labia) and the clitoris.

13

What Adolescents Should Know About Reproduction

by ISADORE RUBIN, PH.D.

It is quite surprising in this day of seeming openness about sex to learn that many persons grow to maturity—and some even become parents—without knowing what it is that brings about conception and pregnancy. Certainly it is essential that young people learn the facts, not only to protect them during their period of adolescence but to prepare them to function adequately in marriage.

Conception takes place when a male sperm pierces a female egg and the two cells join together to begin the creation of a new being. Just how does this process take place? Let us begin with the story of the egg, or *ovum* (plural *ova*). The egg, which is many times smaller than the period at the end of this sentence, is produced in the ovaries, a pair of glands, each about the size of an almond, lying close to the side walls of the pelvic cavity. It has been estimated that the average number of eggs contained in each ovary of the mature woman is about 200,000—making a total of 400,000 eggs in both ovaries.

Once each month, on the average, a mature ovum is discharged from its case, known as the *Graafian follicle*. At this point, the follicle bulges from the ovary wall, which has become very thin, and the egg gently breaks through the ovarian wall. This process, known as *ovulation,* usually alternates in each ovary. Occasionally, however, both ovaries release an egg, or two eggs are released by one ovary during the same month, which makes possible the birth of nonidentical twins. The ovaries of the average woman develop and release about 400 ova during her reproductive lifetime. The remainder of the 400,000 degenerate and disappear. When the woman becomes pregnant, ovulation ceases.

The fertile male is fertile at all times, since sperm are produced constantly and discharged with each ejaculation of semen. In the case of the female, however, there is only a short period each month when she can become pregnant—the time when an egg is released from the ovary. Since the egg can live only a few hours after discharge from the ovary—its maximum life span probably does not exceed thirty-six hours—fertilization can only take place during those few hours, plus the equal period of time during which the sperm can remain alive in the woman's reproductive passages.

Thus, there is usually only a two- or three-day period during each monthly cycle when conception can occur. Abstention from intercourse at this time is utilized as a system of birth control by those who follow the "rhythm method." That period other than the three or four days *before* and *after* ovulation is known as the "safe period." However, the "safe period" is not really safe because ovulation does not always take place at the same time each month. Although the usual time is the midpoint of the monthly cycle, there are considerable variations that can be brought about by emotional stress and other bodily factors. Thus women have been known to conceive at every point in the cycle, including in very rare cases during the period of menstruation itself.

After the egg is released from the ovary, it enters the *Fallopian* tube (there are two of these, one extending from each ovary) and proceeds to move through it. If intercourse has taken place and sperm are present in the tube, the egg may be pierced by the sperm and then fertilization will take place. The fertilized egg— now called a *zygote*—begins to develop as it continues its passage through the tube to the womb, a process that takes about eight or nine days. The fertilized egg then implants itself in the wall of the womb and continues its development. What happens to the egg if no sperm are present to fertilize it? It merely continues on its way and disintegrates in passage and is absorbed.

Once the ovum has been discharged, its case produces a hormone that acts to prepare the womb for possible reception of a fertilized egg. If pregnancy takes place, menstruation stops and no more eggs are released. If pregnancy does not take place, the lining of the womb, which is not needed for nourishing a fertilized egg, is shed and passes out of the body as part of the menstrual discharge.

Now back to the male sperm, or *spermatozoa*. These tiny threadlike cells are produced in an almost never-ending quantity in the normal male. Like saliva, they are not "used up," despite the fact that a single emission of normal semen (the sperm plus the secretion furnished by various glands) contains from 400 to 500 million sperm. The testicles produce the sperm in the approximately 300 sections of microscopic tube that make up the *seminiferous* (seed-bearing) *tubules*. Uncoiled, this network of tubes in the testicles would extend almost a mile.

Surprisingly, the normal temperature of the human body is too high for sperm production. For this reason, the scrotum, a bag with its own mechanism to regulate temperature, is found outside the body. When the temperature is low, a special muscle contracts to bring the testicles closer to the warmth of the body. When it is hot, the muscle lowers the scrotum away from the body. The result is a scrotal temperature that is a few degrees lower than body temperature.

This has led doctors to advise men who have a fertility problem to take special precautions. While most men retain full fertility even though they take prolonged hot baths or Turkish baths, some men of low fertility might suffer impaired sperm production from these practices and are advised to avoid them. It is also advisable for men with a fertility problem not to wear tight-fitting underwear or trousers, which will press the testicles against the body.

The sperm have a long trip to make before they reach the point of ejaculation. They must first travel from the tubules where they are produced to the tail of the coiled body known as the *epididymis*—a twenty-foot trip that may take two weeks to complete. From there they must traverse the eighteen-inch length of the sperm duct—a voyage whose duration has not yet been entirely established. The vastness of the journey the sperm must take can be judged when one considers the size of the average sperm—it must traverse 500 times its own length just to travel one inch. Each inch can be compared to a man's swimming one mile.

When intercourse takes place and semen is ejaculated into the vagina, the millions of sperm in the semen begin to make their way into the neck of the womb, through the womb and into the tubes. If there is no egg in the tubes, the sperm simply begin to disintegrate. If an egg is present, then conception may take place. Some young people believe that pregnancy cannot take place if ejaculation occurs outside the vagina. But in such cases it is possible for the sperm to make their way into the vagina even through the minute openings of an unbroken hymen, the thin membrane that usually stretches across the virgin's vagina just within its entrance.

There are a number of methods and devices to prevent conception from taking place. These include abstention from intercourse during the ovulation period ("rhythm method"), mechanical devices to prevent the sperm from entering the womb (condoms and diaphragm), chemical devices to kill the sperm in the vagina (foams, powders, and gels), *coitus interruptus*—withdrawal of penis before ejaculation takes place, a method to prevent an egg from being released by the ovary (pills), and devices to interfere with fertilization and implantation of the egg within the womb (intrauterine rings and coils). Not all of these methods or devices are equally effective, and the last-named is recommended only after a woman has had one child. The "best" method for any particular couple is that one which is most suited to their particular desires, feelings, and temperaments, the one they will use most faithfully and responsibly.

14

Adolescents and Contraception

Part I: Should Adolescents Learn About Contraception?

by ISADORE RUBIN, PH.D.

One of the most controversial aspects of sex education is the question of contraception. Many parents who recognize that learning about birth control and family planning is an important part of preparation for marriage are still beset by gnawing doubts. Won't this kind of information undercut their ethical teachings about sex? Some critics see such education about contraception as an invitation to youngsters to engage in more premarital sex relations since the fear of pregnancy would be removed. Apparently these parents and critics believe that fear is a great deterrent against sex activity and that ignorance or lack of preparation is a safeguard. Is this belief supported by the body of our experience?

Speaking at a conference on abortion, the late Alfred C. Kinsey pointed out that many of the unwanted pregnancies occurred among the religiously devout who set out on a date with the determination that they were not going to be sinful and engage in intercourse. With such a conviction in mind, they did not carry contraceptives. They ended up by having coitus, Dr. Kinsey remarked, and "thus we see in some of the most devout . . . extramarital pregnancies, leading ultimately to abortion or to forced marriage."

KNOWLEDGE ABOUT CONTRACEPTION AND THE INCIDENCE OF PREMARITAL SEX

If knowledge about contraception were a major factor in encouraging sex relations, one would expect that college students—who obviously know most about contraception—would engage in premarital intercourse in the greatest numbers. The fact is, however, as every survey has shown, that a much smaller proportion of college students engage in premarital sex relations than do those who never go beyond elementary school.

All evidence, also, points to the fact that fear has never been a major deterrent to sexual relations, as any army doctor can show. Although some soldiers fainted at the horror-filled films depicting the dangers of venereal disease, the figures on VD do not furnish any evidence that these films actually had any effect. At the World Forum on Syphilis, held in 1962, John Gagnon of the Kinsey Institute for Sex Research presented convincing documentation proving that fear had been of minimum effectiveness in keeping persons from engaging in sexual intercourse. For example, he pointed out, when VD was a really dread disease and its cure was neither swift nor sure, fear did not keep males from engaging in sexual contact.

Gagnon reported that as part of their study of the sex offender, the researchers collected premarital histories of nondelinquent males. They found that of those who expressed *no* fear of venereal disease, 15.4 per cent had contracted it. Of those expressing *moderate* fear, the percentages *rose* to 20.8 per cent, while 15.3 per cent of those with *strong* fear had been infected. These figures clearly indicate how small a role fear plays as far as the male is concerned.

Undoubtedly, many girls have been kept from engaging in sexual intercourse because of fear of pregnancy, but, as the Kinsey studies showed, moral considerations are of primary importance. Michael Schofield's most recent study (1965) of the behavior of young people in England showed that while sexually experienced girls expressed considerable fear of pregnancy, this fear had not kept them from having sexual relations.

Actually, experience shows that in a great many cases it is not knowledge about contraception that leads to sexual intercourse but rather the reverse. In London, where birth-control clinics for unmarried persons were established, it was found that most of the young people who came for contraceptive advice had already been engaging in sexual intercourse for a considerable period of time. Often they came to the clinic when they began to feel a deepened sense of responsibility toward each other.

The issue is really not one of ignorance *versus* information, but one of getting information given carefully by responsible sources as opposed to getting it from poorly informed friends or irresponsible sources. Who has not heard stories of young boys who have used plastic wrap as a contraceptive, of girls who have douched with soda pop, and of others who have taken a few of their mothers' birth-control pills? Today, when so many bits of information or misinformation are available in one way or another, it makes sense to provide young persons with a thorough knowledge of contraception in order to counter the dangers of any smattering of incomplete or incorrect knowledge that they may pick up.

But knowledge by itself is not enough to ensure that the information will be put to use; it is the individual's attitudes that will determine this. In the British study by Schofield, 82 per cent of the sexually experienced girls said they knew something about the sort of precautions people take to avoid pregnancy, but less than 0.5 per cent (just 3 in all) had ever purchased a contraceptive, and nearly all of them left it to the boy to decide what form of birth control he would use, if any. Many girls still prefer to feel that they are being swept off their feet by passion; if they were to concern themselves with contraception, they feel, they would be like prostitutes. Certainly it will take us a long time to free ourselves from the historic association between contraceptive devices and obscenity.

Some parents are afraid that if they teach their children directly how contraceptives are used, this might very well be interpreted by the youngsters as encouragement to engage in premarital sex. This is a legitimate fear, particularly if the parents have waited until their children have reached the age where they must begin to make decisions about sexual activity. This, however, is an argument, not in favor of no education but of earlier education. Psychiatric thinking suggests that the best time for the youngster to receive factual information about such subjects is the period in which his emotions in respect to that information are dormant or less involved.

Also, the most effective kind of teaching by the parents need not be at all direct. They need not talk *at* their youngsters. In fact, at this age, particularly, indirect education may be far more effective. There are many teachable moments in everyday home life when a discussion about birth control can be initiated. Almost daily the papers discuss some aspect of the "population explosion" or the various campaigns to publicize birth control. Very often an occasion will present itself—one of the parents may have heard about an abortion that was performed or a friend who has gotten pregnant. Parents can discuss these situations among themselves or with friends in the presence of the youngsters. They may be sure that the children will avidly listen to what they say and they will take the information more seriously than lectures directed at them.

But it is in our schools that such education can be most effectively conducted. Here youngsters can learn scientifically about birth control as part of preparation for marriage. Certainly under the proper conditions, young people will not consider such instruction an invitation for them to engage in sexual activities.

All major studies have shown that it is not fear and ignorance that result in desirable behavior, but the moral and ethical beliefs that one has been taught since childhood—a sense of what is right and wrong about sex. Parents should therefore place their trust in building a positive set of sexual values rather than relying on fear and ignorance as deterrents.

Part II: Contraception and Responsibility

by AARON L. RUTLEDGE, TH.D.

Will detailed knowledge about contraception encourage young people to have sexual intercourse? I doubt this very much, especially if they have been brought up with an intelligently spelled out and demonstrated set of ideals. In fact, if youngsters are taught not to have sexual intercourse without taking birth control into account, they might even be deterred.

Stopping to think about and apply a contraceptive device is, for both the boy and girl, a chance to consider whether or not to go ahead with intercourse. In the buildup of passion, remembering the necessity of preventing conception can become a cold fact of reality to jar them back to awareness.

It is natural to feel that if youngsters are going to have sexual intercourse then, by all means, they should avoid pregnancy. If contraception has been learned about accidentally, it will be used unwisely if at all. In fact, when learned about in this way, young people often have a disdain for the use of any contraception. They tend to take a more foolhardy attitude, believing that they can get away with it.

Young girls should grow into womanhood with a sense of responsibility for the eggs they produce in their bodies. There are times, places, and circumstances for the conception, growth, and development of a child. There are other times when this would be a tragedy for everybody concerned. It seems like good adjustment and responsible behavior for a girl to take measures to prevent conception, when she has decided to have intercourse. It probably is best that she grow up with the conviction that in order to plan the reproductive aspects of her life she must always take into account contraceptive knowledge.

It is just as important that the boy have a similar attitude of responsibility for his sperm. The more popular belief is that this is the girl's problem; the only worry the boy has is the fear of an unwanted forced marriage. Such an attitude of irresponsibility, such an imposition upon the girl and her welfare, is a disturbing trait in so many young men today. A young man should grow up being aware that he is responsible for his actions. Does he want to be the father of a child who will be reared by a girl outside of marriage? Does he want to be the cause of bringing a child into the world who will have to be placed in an agency? Does he want to be the cause of pushing a girl into an abortion?

For the boy and the girl, the first place to learn about birth control is within the home as part of the ethical teachings of the parents. One of the primary reasons for giving contraceptive information at an early age is the influence this will have upon the individuals later in marriage.

Over and over we see women who will not trust contraception because they were never helped to understand and accept it. Others will employ contraception, accept it intellectually, but will never quite relax and freely enjoy sexual relations because they have not accepted it emotionally. The girl should grow up sexually with the realization that contraceptives will be a part of her sexual life until she has passed menopause. The young man should grow up with the expectation that some sort of contraceptive will be a required part of his sex life, too.

Part V

Helping the Younger Adolescent Cope with Sexual Needs

15

What Parents Should Do About Masturbation

by ISADORE RUBIN, PH.D.

A great many parents, by now, have become aware of the fact that masturbation is a normal part of growing up and does not have—in any way, physically or mentally—a harmful effect. They have read, time and again, that the only ill effect that may result is an emotional upset that comes, not from the act itself but from the fact that children have been made to feel guilty about "touching themselves" and have been punished, shamed, or threatened because of it.

But a myth dies very hard. It is impossible to wash away in one generation almost two thousand years of encrusted teaching that every form of sex activity without the purpose of procreation is sinful. For well over two centuries, leading medical men have believed that masturbation led to insanity. Within the lifetime of many persons now alive, doctors were prescribing such drastic measures for preventing masturbation as castration, amputation of the clitoris, removal of the ovary, cutting the genital nerve supply, and tying the sperm ducts!

Thus it is shocking—but not surprising—that even in leading medical schools today large numbers of students—and even professors—have not been able to rid themselves entirely of the old beliefs about masturbation. And many well-meaning family doctors still give parents advice that grows out of outworn notions rather than modern medical science.

"EXCESSIVE MASTURBATION"

Fortunately many authorities in the field of child development and guidance are beginning to emphasize a more scientific and objective attitude. For example, Dr. John Oliven in his book *Sexual Hygiene and Pathology,* a standard manual for physicians, suggests the following: "As a general rule, it is probably best to advise parents to disregard evidence of masturbation in juveniles, not to 'look for it' nor to try to prevent it."

Very often parents will tell their children that masturbation is not harmful "if not practiced too often." This is a mistake, says Dr. Benjamin Spock, the noted expert on child care. "There is no medical basis for this distinction," he points out, "and it only shifts the worry of the child to the question of what is 'too often.' "

Other authorities, like Drs. Milton I. Levine and Anita I. Bell, suggest to the pediatrician that he "must emphasize the rôle of masturbation as a normal physiologic function which is at maximum intensity between the ages of 3 and 6 years and again during puberty." These specialists in child development emphasize that when not excessive "masturbatory activity in childhood may be considered as entirely normal, and in adolescence as a normal outlet for suppressed heterosexual urges."

As to the phrase "excessive masturbation," they point out that while many authors have used the expression, no one, as Dr. Kinsey noted, has really defined what "excessive masturbation" is.

According to Drs. Levine and Bell, masturbation in children and adolescents is "excessive" only when the activity is repeated with such frequency during the waking hours that most other activities are excluded. It does not include the child who engages in the act only when going to sleep. When self-relief is excessive (as they define it), these two physicians view it as a symptom of the child's unhappiness or emotional instability. In such cases, it is not so much the act itself as the original emotional upset which is harmful and must be treated. Masturbation is a release of various tension states in the individual.

Parents should realize that even very young infants can experience sensory pleasures and get pleasurable sensations when their genitals are manipulated. In the course of random movements, the infant discovers that contact with the genitals is pleasurable. Sometimes the infant scratches or rubs to stop itching or discomfort, discovers the sensation is pleasant, and continues. One doctor reported that the practice of masturbation in one child began when it was only one week old.

WHAT PARENTS SHOULD DO

What should parents do about masturbation in children? First of all, they should accept it completely and without reservation. They should not say, "Yes, we know there's nothing wrong with it," and then search for devious methods of preventing masturbation when they find children practicing it. This policy should be followed for infants, youngsters, and adolescents alike. At no time should the child be scolded, spanked, shamed, or threatened in any way. Prohibition and punishment do not make the child engage less in masturbation; on the contrary, they lead to greater indulgence in this practice. Some children will lie awake at night in order to practice masturbation secretly, if they are forbidden to do so during the day. Many will indulge in the habit extensively to make up for lost time or out of spite.

Masturbation or manipulation is often a response to tension. Prohibition and punishment lead to more tension, hence a greater need for the release which can be gotten through masturbation. Of course, if there are any physical conditions which bring about irritation of the genitals in the young child—too-tight clothing, etc.—these conditions should be corrected. And in those rare cases where the child seems to be devoting all his time to masturbation, the parent should find out whether psychological help is needed.

As far as adolescents are concerned, masturbation is practiced more frequently by those young people who do not engage in sex relations. Thus it is basically a substitute sexual outlet for most adolescents who are compelled to postpone their sexual satisfaction, for the most part, until marriage.

Most boys—and a large percentage of girls—have masturbated at least occasionally during the period of adolescence. Because of the generally unfavorable attitude of society, many youngsters are greatly troubled by the fact that they cannot resist the urge to masturbate. One study of college women found that masturbation was the most difficult aspect of sex for them to discuss.

Parents should find some nonmechanical way of communicating to their adolescent children the attitude that there is nothing wrong with masturbation physically or psychologically. The question "Is it morally wrong?" has to be answered, of course, by each parent on the basis of his own personal beliefs, but it is important for young persons to recognize that masturbation represents an important and normal aspect of psychosexual development.

16

The First Love Affair

by JOHN B. THOMPSON

The family is a strange institution: it is at one and the same time the creative source of life's highest values and the seedbed of most of our serious problems of maladjustment. A queer commentary on our civilization is the fact that many of the things we do to our adolescent boys and girls tend to thwart rather than to encourage the process of maturing. The average parent would not dream of making fun of the youngster when his teeth begin to appear or when his first set of teeth drop out. Yet when symptoms of the first love affair begin to appear—symptoms as natural, normal, and inevitable as the change of teeth—the modern family becomes primitive in a way that maligns primitive man and rivals his ability to be cruel.

None of us would be cruel enough to make fun of the child for physical changes and growth; yet when Tommy begins to comb his hair with extraordinary care and Peggy exhibits a precocious interest in nail polish; or when Bill changes rather suddenly from a he-man, cowboy, or Indian fighter into a moony young swain of pimples and poetry—then the great American family drags out the torture instruments and to the natural pains of gawkiness and mystifying growth we add the unnecessary torture of derision and silly ridicule.

My thesis can be put in two or three very simple propositions. The first is this: that the first love affair—and the second and third and tenth for that matter—*are an expression of natural drives and emotions which if not present and voting in your child's life would leave him deprived, abnormal, and to be pitied.*

If, from the parent's viewpoint, the adolescent's emotional life seems difficult, think for a moment what it would be without these changes. Think of the dull monotony of a life without radical changes in emotional tone, or of the tragedy of the feeble-minded child who never outgrows infancy; and then give thanks if your adolescent children raise the roof now and then and keep you awake nights wondering if you were as silly as they are at this age.

Secondly, *the first love affair is inevitably the family's affair.* Up to adolescence every experience is a group experience, and what the family group does to the individual as he becomes more conscious of his individuality will determine major characteristics and attitudes all through his life.

Therefore, this problem of the youngster's first love affair is essentially a problem in maturing, and it requires maturing on the part of the parents fully as much as on the part of the youngster. The adolescent will mature naturally if you give him half a chance; but it is very difficult for some parents to stop babying and patronizing their children and allow them to grow up.

POINTS OF GROWTH REVEALED IN THE FIRST LOVE AFFAIR

There are three important points of growth which are revealed in the family's first love affair, and which call for genuine maturing both on the part of the children and on the part of the parents.

The first is *the growth of the independence motive in the adoles-*

cent himself. This motive is strong in these years of the early teens; and something is wrong with the youngster who doesn't want to become free from adult domination. The drives behind the first love affair are not nearly so much the desire to find a partner for life as the desire to be a little more independent of the small family group and to make some important judgments and decisions. It ought to be obvious that a child can never develop self-reliance until he is allowed to practice some independence and self-assertion.

If treated sensibly, the first love affair will not be exaggerated out of all proportion, but will simply be one of a number of ways in which the growing youngster experimentally earns his rightful freedom and independence of judgment. It is as important as learning to cross the road without the parent's hand to pilot him. Instead of making discipline more and more strict as the adolescent begins to declare his independence, the wise parent will help provide areas where this spirit of 1776 can be adequately and wholesomely expressed in the family itself.

A second point of growth is *the adolescent's new expression of the group spirit.* It is natural for the boy to want to belong to a "gang" and for the girl to have her cliques. It is also natural for the growing youngster to enlarge his circle of interest and of social activity to include youngsters of the opposite sex. Youth needs such activity. He does this for a great number of reasons. It is obviously more healthy for him to be interested in other people than to be preoccupied with himself all the time; no one wants his boy to turn into a little narcissus, priggishly stuck on himself. It is obvious, also, that one way to get group approval (which the adolescent needs as much as he needs oxygen) is to develop strong friendships and in due time to fall in love.

Not many youngsters fall into a lifetime passion at the tender age of nine as did the great Italian poet Dante. Even in the teens most adolescents are more interested in the idea of falling in love than they are in the persons who are temporarily the object of their melodramatic affections. The worst and most irrelevant tool that could be used in such periods is the tool of logic. It is heartless and irrelevant for a sophisticated and jaded adult to chide the adolescent for his inconstancy, or to invade the sanctity of his moony dreamings by asserting that, of course, he is not really in love and the object of his affections is not a suitable life-mate for him, and so on.

In the first love affairs the average youngster is not hunting a life-mate. He is giving valid expression to his desire to be independent, to his drive to be social, to his desire to win social approval, and to his normal impulses to grow up. The mother who wants to be her son's only sweetheart until he is sixteen ought to see a psychiatrist. The parent who resents the fifteen-year-old boy's romantic love, no matter how silly and trite it may appear to an observer, should realize that any thwarting of such tendencies would prolong infantile attitudes. The youngster who is thwarted or ridiculed in this first wild, careless, and awkward rapture is often incapable of ever having the thoroughly normal, happy love life that he deserves later in life. If you keep your daughter as isolated as the sleeping beauty, no fairy prince is likely to come along, and even if he should, the girl wouldn't know how to respond unless she had first had a lot of experience playing games and attending parties with all kinds of flesh-and-blood knights.

Finally, *the adolescent's first love affair involves growth of sex-consciousness and interest.* This aspect of maturing should be neither neglected nor overemphasized. It is unfortunate when the whole process of adolescence is interpreted exclusively in terms of physical maturing. It is likewise unfortunate when the youngster is allowed to reach his teens without having had progressive, natural, regular experience of wholesome sex instruction. Whereas, during an earlier age the interest in the opposite sex has been nil; or whereas, the junior boys have regarded their girl playmates as unimportant nuisances and the girls have thought of the boys as neuter hoodlums; suddenly another idea dawns on the horizon. To the girl a certain boy at school is unutterably "cute"; he is a swell athlete or perhaps he looks like Marlon Brando. To a boy a certain girl is not only worth looking at twice but is worth mooning about.

The wise adult refrains from casting aspersions on these experiences, and refrains from distorting their normal significance by announcing Freudian interpretations. The wise parent knows that the first love affair will probably be of short duration but that it is extremely important; for whenever the child fails to be accepted and approved in the first association with the opposite sex, for any reason whatever, then very important developments may be thwarted or twisted for years to come.

On the other hand the sex factor should not be emphasized by the adult when it is not emphasized by the child. It is not fair for the older brother to accuse the little sister of dark and sinister sex motives whenever she first experiments with rogue and lipstick. There are scores of vague and mixed motives behind her venture; she is not suddenly changed from the Age of Innocence into a designing woman out on the warpath to get her man!

The only possible way to avert abnormalities and unhappiness in later life is to provide full and free opportunities for uncriticized gawkiness and uncondemned foolishness in adolescence. We who counsel college students frequently find that failures to make normal and wholesome adjustments in their social life at the university, or in their adult love affairs, lead relentlessly and unmistakably back to frustrations and unhappy aspects of their first childhood love affairs.

A person does not suddenly become an adult at the age of twenty-one. Learning to deal with life on a plane of maturity and intelligence is a learning process; just as slow, and as difficult, as learning to swim or to sew. No mother teaching her daughter to sew would ridicule the first awkward attempts to handle the needle. If that were the mother's response, the daughter would never learn to sew. Why, then, can not parents themselves become mature enough in their attitudes toward the first love affair to make the child's maturing less painful and more wholesome and happy?

17

Pro's and Con's of Petting

by ROBERT A. HARPER, PH.D.

In modern society, *petting* has been adopted as the term for physical contacts (short of sexual intercourse) designed to bring sexual arousal and/or sexual satisfaction. The behavior patterns designated as petting antedate the human species. Since noncoital sex play is not only a universal phenomenon among mammals, but is common among vertebrates of lower evolutionary classes, such as birds and reptiles, it is quite evident that petting is biologically rooted in a normal and natural way in the sensory satisfactions that derive from various types of bodily contact.

All of the petting techniques known to modern generations are found in the art and writings of ancient civilizations. In like manner, reports from anthropologists and other observers of preliterate peoples indicate the widespread presence of the same behavior patterns that we call petting.

And, while the student of the early history of American society will not find references to petting under that name, he will find descriptions of such activities among our colonial ancestors under various designations like spooning, sparking, smooching, bundling, lolligagging, mugging, larking, flirtage, and courting.

It seemed to me desirable to write briefly of the biological and historical roots of petting in order to make two points clear at the outset. First of all, no rational case can be made that petting is a perverted and decadent invention of the present generation of American youth. Such contentions have nevertheless occasionally been made by so-called authorities as well as by many laymen. Secondly, petting is so deeply ingrained in human nature that it would be foolish indeed for us to assume that any "pro" or "con" position we take regarding it will have a fundamental effect on its presence in modern American society (or any other society).

Many youths and their parents, however, would like to have help in thinking through the desirabilities and undesirabilities of petting. To offer an analogy, we may agree that a certain amount of anger or boredom or indigestion is unavoidable in the course of a lifetime. Is petting, like any one of these analogous conditions, something to be discouraged or avoided in the boy-girl relationships prior to marriage? Or is petting something desirable to be sought after by young people? I shall present the main arguments for and against premarital petting and let the reader draw his own conclusions. I shall forego editorial comment on what I consider the soundness or unsoundness of the various pro and con contentions, but I shall tell you my own convictions at the end of the chapter.

THE CASE FOR PETTING

The chief constructive significance of petting would seem to lie in the opportunities it provides to youth to learn the art of loving. It is not only the first source of specific sexual arousal and of orgasm for many girls in our society, but it is the main, broad sociosexual educative force for young people of both sexes. Such education and practical experience in love expression are crucially needed by American youth because of the tendency in our society to induce drastic inhibition of erotic feelings in the period from infancy through puberty.

Many boys and girls in America grow up not only with strong sanctions against the direct and intimate feelings of affection, but with outright distrust and hostility toward members of the other sex. Some type of permissive setting where adolescents may learn to relate to members of the other sex and to develop some degree of freedom and spontaneity in the expression of affection would seem to be a cultural desirability.

The taboos against premarital petting in American society are particularly unfortunate in light of the even stronger moral sanctions against premarital sexual intercourse. In a cultural environment where premarital coitus was not heavily condemned, sanctions against premarital petting would be of distinctly less significance. It certainly seems to be an absurd procedure for a society, first, to instill strong sexual inhibitions in children and, then, to try to cut off both coital and noncoital avenues for adolescents to learn to overcome such inhibitions prior to sexual functioning in marriage. This is exactly what our society has officially attempted. The "success" of the official program, however, lies chiefly in its induction of guilt feelings in some young people who pet, more than in the prevention of petting.

To state the positive case for premarital petting more specifically, it offers the opportunity for young people to learn particular love-making techniques and responses to various types of persons of the other sex. In marriage, little chance is usually offered for the gradual acquisition of skill in, and unembarrassed ease in responding to such activities as kissing, deep kissing, breast and genital fondling, oral-genital contacts, etc., that youth can take their time in learning in the course of premarital relationships. Absence of comfortable acceptance of such love-making procedures may be interpreted as rejection by the more experienced marital partner, on the one hand, and quick introduction of such activities in marriage may frighten and induce sexual withdrawal on the part of a very inexperienced partner. Such feelings of rejection and withdrawal often permanently mar a marital relationship.

It is sometimes contended that premarital petting may lead to marriage on strictly sexual bases. Such petting may, on the contrary, provide young people with an opportunity to respond over a considerable period of time to a fairly representative sample of persons of the other sex and thus come to know the kind of persons to whom they are permanently attracted in both an erotic and broader affectionate way. A fairly expansive premarital sexual experience would appear to provide a background against which young people can make sounder marital choices. The sexually experienced would logically appear better prepared not to be misled by temporary erotic urges than the sexually inexperienced.

THE CASE AGAINST PETTING

It is generally wise for couples who are considering marriage to spend a good portion of their time together in situations which make romantic activity difficult. If courting couples spend most of their time making love, or most of their time in any other single-line pursuit, they are not likely to learn much about the kind of personality characteristics that are important in making for non-sexual compatibility or incompatibility in close day-by-day living.

Petting tends to cheapen sex and romance, to emphasize the biological rather than the spiritual aspects of love. Young people who allow themselves to become addicts to it tend to exaggerate the importance of sex during the premarital period. If the boy and girl truly love each other on the basis of a long and varied companionship, sex responses will readily take care of themselves in marriage.

Although boys often try to coax or argue girls into petting with them, many of these young men do not themselves approve of or respect girls who do pet. A girl, therefore, who hopes to use petting as a means to popularity, or as a route to marriage, may find that the results are quite the opposite of her expectations.

Chronic petting may have undesirable physiological effects. Headaches, backaches, abdominal pains, and sleepiness are among the reported results of frequent petting.

Petting may lead to sexual intercourse, with the combined problems of moral guilt and possible pregnancy. Even though young people resolve to stop short of coitus, the direct stimulation of their sex urges is likely to lead them to forget their resolutions to remain virginal.

On the other hand, the couple may pet themselves to a point of sexual arousal which has no prospect of adequate release or satisfaction. This has been likened to being "all dressed up with no place to go." The effects of such habitual arousal and frustration may be hypersensitivity and increased irritability, and such effects may strain and break a relationship that was otherwise sound and might have led to successful marriage.

Even if the foregoing hazards of petting are avoided or minimized by a particular couple, that couple may go on to base its marriage primarily on sexual attraction. A marriage which has its chief base in sexual attraction is not likely to be a sound one. Sexual excitement tends to wane after the early stages of marriage, and a husband and wife who married chiefly for this reason may wake up to find that they have nothing else there for a happy future together.

Since many young people are brought up to feel that petting is wrong, proceeding to do so causes serious emotional conflict for some of these persons. Not a few of our youth feel quite guilty after having petted. Even if a particular individual has no such guilt feelings himself, he may bring forth such reactions in his petting partner.

Another argument against petting is that it may constitute a form of sexual deviation. When it becomes so entrenched as a habit that it is invariably preferred (even after marriage) to all other forms of sex relations and is insisted upon as the exclusive means of achieving orgasm, petting may be considered a form of sexual fetichism, compulsiveness, or neurosis.

Although it is not too likely, petting couples can run afoul of the law in most jurisdictions in the United States. Many of the so-called heavy-petting techniques are in many places technically defined as criminal even in marital relationships. Also when a minor is involved with an adult, the minor is subject to prosecution for juvenile delinquency and the adult for contributing to the delinquency of a minor. Where the petting takes place in a public situation, the participants are subject to prosecution for public indecency or disorderly conduct. Where two young people of approximately the same age level are involved, police in most jurisdictions are usually satisfied with "breaking it up" and "scaring them off" (with, perhaps, undesirable psychological but not legal consequences).

Those, then, are the main arguments made in and out of the professional literature for and against premarital petting. Whether or not anything is right or wrong depends, of course, upon social attitudes in regard to it. Attitudes in regard to petting vary widely in our society today. In relation to this and many other sexual matters our values are in the process of change. Many older people think petting among unmarried youth is definitely immoral. Others consider it merely inadvisable or dangerous (on such grounds as those we have just briefly described). The consensus of the younger generation seems to be that it is an individual matter, and opinion varies widely as to the circumstances under which the particular young person considers petting right or wrong. In short, present-day American society has no unequivocal answer on the rightness or wrongness of this question.

THE AUTHOR'S VIEWS

Before we considered the arguments for and against premarital petting, I stated that I would present my own point of view. It is this: I believe that most of the arguments against petting boil down to a prudish or puritanical nonacceptance of sex as a wholesome human attribute. I think most, if not all, of the "bad" or "immoral" aspects of petting are a result of parents and other adults instilling in children and adolescents the belief that sex is strictly for procreation in marriage and not for enjoyment as a human being in or out of marriage.

As a result of some youth's sense of guilt about petting, then, of course, "bad" consequences in these youth occur. This probably includes some psychosomatic effects like headaches, backaches, and the like. But to attribute such effects to petting rather than to deliberately instilled guilt about petting is to engage, I believe, in false and unfair reasoning.

It is also true, as I see it, that many of the undesirable effects of premarital petting are indirectly related to prudishness in the sense that many young people are made to feel that it is more wrong to pet to orgasm than to stop short of orgasm. This makes petting an unnecessarily frustrating experience.

The most serious argument against petting in the eyes of many parents with whom I have counseled is that a permissive attitude about petting is apt to make sexual intercourse more likely for their children. *This, in my experience, is a false argument.* It is again based on the assumption that petting will not proceed to orgasm. If petting proceeds to full climax, then sexual intercourse is much less apt to occur, for the couple will be reasonably satisfied. Another answer to the point that coitus is more apt to result from petting than when petting is not engaged in are the findings of

Kinsey and his associates. Their studies clearly indicate that petting is much more frequently engaged in by youth of the higher educational and higher income groups than among the less educated and lower income groups. Premarital sexual intercourse, on the other hand, has a much higher incidence in the very groups who engage in the least amount of premarital petting. Hence, the idea that the latter leads to the former would seem quite illogical.

Part VI

*Helping Young People
Establish Sex Standards
and Values*

18

The Importance of Moral Codes

by ISADORE RUBIN, PH.D.

Both from the point of view of society and of the individual, the problem of moral values is crucial in any program of sex education. Since sex constitutes a drive of such strength and importance and since its effects almost always concern more than one person, no society that we know of has ever permitted sex behavior to be entirely a matter of individual choice; all societies have regulated it in important ways. This does not mean that all, or even a majority of them, proscribed sex before marriage. Most of them were concerned with preventing a child from being born to a couple that were not married.

Many young people see moral rules only as restrictions, as the bars of a prison. However, as Dr. Sylvanus M. Duvall has pointed out, the basic function of rules is to be a kind of road map. As he says:

Not only children, but most adults cannot know in advance where different policy roads are likely to lead. They often lack the knowledge and the experience to know why certain things should be done, or not done. In some instances, such as running through a red light at high speed, no harm has resulted. It is only as a policy that it would be disastrous. In other instances, as in a vitamin deficient diet, the individual cannot see why he should be restricted or regulated. The function of rules . . . is to let people know the kinds of policies of behavior that, on the whole, will prove harmful or beneficial.

While recognizing the importance of moral rules, parents and teachers must also take into account the fact that young people are increasingly unlikely to accept the old black-and-white distinctions between "moral" and "immoral" behavior. Rigid and absolute commandments do not offer much appeal in today's complex world, particularly since thinking in absolute terms is more and more contradicted by the results of research and experience. In the past, there was a tendency to think that the results of any form of behavior were inherent in the behavior itself, without in any way considering the situation in which the behavior took place or the moral codes held by the people participating in that behavior. Thus there was a tendency, for example, to discuss the effect of premarital sex without distinguishing between the various kinds of premarital sex: with a prostitute, with a casual pickup, between an engaged couple, etc. Today we know—particularly from research done by Dr. Lester Kirkendall—that, without making such distinctions, the discussion becomes meaningless. Premarital sex between an engaged couple committed to each other is wholly different in meaning and effect from sex between a young man and a casual pickup.

A PERSON'S ATTITUDE TOWARD PREMARITAL SEX AFFECTS HOW HE FEELS AFTER ENGAGING IN IT

How a person feels about premarital sex makes a tremendous difference in the effect which engaging in it has. A young person who has been raised in a family which believes that there is something terribly wrong with sex before marriage and engages in it against his own moral beliefs and convictions is quite likely to suffer in some way from such behavior. This would not be true of an individual raised to believe that sex before marriage is not intrinsically wrong and a matter of personal choice.

Dr. Harold T. Christensen has compared the extent and effects of premarital intercourse among college students in three different cultures. One was a culture that was relatively free and permissive in its attitudes toward sex before marriage—Denmark. A second was a group in an Indiana college that represented more or less typical American attitudes, while the third was from a Mormon community, from one of the most restrictive groups in the United States.

Dr. Christensen found that by a number of measures, those students from the most restrictive culture suffered most from engaging in premarital sex because they were violating the most strongly held moral beliefs. In the first place, they suffered most guilt and other negative reactions from the experience. When premarital pregnancy took place, they were pressured most quickly into marriage. Finally, the effect of premarital sex upon divorce rates was greatest for them. In each case, the negative consequences in Denmark, the most permissive culture, was the lowest of the three groups studied. Dr. Christensen's research suggests quite clearly that it is behavior that violates one's moral beliefs which is most damaging and that young persons must be encouraged to act in accordance with their own personal moral codes rather than to give in to pressure of others. This holds true not only for premarital intercourse, but also for such activities as petting, masturbation, and other kinds of sexual behavior.

THE IMPORTANCE OF A VIABLE MORAL CODE

The importance of moral rules makes it imperative for parents to provide their youngsters with a set of values that can serve as guides for future conduct. What the particular values are that individual parents provide will depend upon their religious beliefs, their attitudes toward sex, and their own upbringing. Young people should also be made aware of what the conventional social codes expect of them since these are important factors in their own decision-making.

Unfortunately, today, our society as a whole is not able to reach general agreement on its moral rules. Almost wherever one turns there is sharp controversy on specific moral policies. This is true whether the issue is birth control, abortion, divorce, artificial insemination, or sexual relations between unmarried persons. Even among religious leaders of the same faith one finds this controversy present. This situation is part of what Dr. Gibson Winter has called the transformation of the sexual sphere from a public morality into a more private responsibility. "We live now," he says, "in the Personal Age of Sexuality."

These new conditions of transition and controversy present the family and the individual with a new situation in respect to moral values. In the past, few persons challenged the official codes in their thinking, even though many violated them in their behavior. Today for the first time almost in history, individuals are being offered a certain freedom to make a choice among moral codes. For the first time as a society we are being forced to live with a diversity of sexual beliefs just as we have been living for a long time with a diversity of religious, social, and political beliefs. This diversity means that parents can no longer expect young people to accept traditional rigid commandments without questioning, examining and evaluating them. Most of our sex codes must now compete in the open marketplace of ideas.

Contrary to what many young people think, this freedom is not easy but brings with it many problems. For if the individual must make many moral decisions of his own, he cannot make such decisions responsibly unless he has sufficient knowledge about the pluses and minuses of each course of behavior. From the earliest days possible it is important for parents to begin to train their youngsters for the task of making these decisions intelligently and responsibly.

In addition to the specific sexual codes which parents may wish to inculcate in their youngsters, there are common values that are basic to a democratic society and that most thoughtful persons will agree upon regardless of their different beliefs. Although these are general moral values, they are particularly applicable in the area of sex during a time of confusion, transition, and personal responsibility. These general values which can be used as important guides in sex conduct include the following: (1) respect for the basic worth, equality and dignity of each individual; (2) accordance of the right of self-determination to each human being; (3) recognition of the need for cooperative effort for the common good; and (4) respect for truth.

Within this moral framework, it can be clearly seen that it is immoral for boys or girls to try to take advantage of or exploit each other sexually. It is immoral for a boy to pretend he is in love with a girl in order to have her give in to him sexually. It is equally immoral for a girl to engage in sexual intercourse in the hope of trapping her partner into marriage. And it is immoral for either to try to pressure the partner into a relationship for which the other is not emotionally prepared.

Basically, each individual must make his own personal decisions about sexual behavior. These decisions should be made in the light of his own moral beliefs and should be based upon clear insight into his own personality needs and convictions. They should not result from the pressures and the beliefs of others.

This moral approach attempts to place sex in context as an important aspect of interpersonal relationships. The central concern is not to encourage or discourage sex activity, but to teach how to use sex positively. The core of the ethical problem is not whether a boy or girl remains or does not remain a virgin, but whether sex is used exploitatively and self-centeredly, or in a meaningful and dignified way.

19

Helping Girls Establish Sex Standards

by LESTER A. KIRKENDALL, PH.D.

Although the popular idea of the "sex revolution" widely exaggerates the extent of teen-age promiscuity, there has been a clear long-term trend for girls to abandon virginity as a sexual standard. This view is given support by information gathered in the Kinsey study. Dr. Kinsey wrote that among females "born before 1900, less than half as many had had premarital coitus as among the females born in any subsequent decade." What is back of this? Are girls just becoming more careless? Are boys becoming more persuasive? Or, are there still other conditions which explain this? Apparently the answer is quite complex; many factors are involved.

First, girls used to be very much more closely supervised in their associations with males than they are now. Courting in the living room, for example, under the watchful eyes of parents or a chaperone, has given way to love-making in a car. In other words the girl of 1963 has to preserve her virginity, if this is what she wishes to do, almost unaided.

Second, the boy who wishes to persuade a virgin girl to have intercourse has much more convincing arguments now than he used to have. Contraceptives are much improved and knowledge about them much more widespread than was the case 60 years ago. The girl is no longer in a position to plead the dangers of pregnancy as convincingly as she formerly could. Neither is the argument that she will be subject to community criticism if she becomes pregnant as strong as it used to be. An unmarried couple known to be engaging in intercourse, or having a premarital pregnancy, may still meet criticism but they will often find some people at least, willing to help them in working out their problem.

Third, girls are apparently more willing to give up their virginity. For a long time we have taught that it was up to the girl to determine how far a dating couple went sexually. She, rather than the boy, had to set the limits. This point of view assumed that girls had no special feelings until she was "awakened," presumably by her husband.

But in recent years quite a confusion has crept into the teaching of teen-age girls concerning their sexuality. At the same time that we have been stressing feminine virginity we have been telling girls that (when married of course, and only then) they, too, have a sexual nature. They can enjoy sex; they have a right to and should expect to enjoy sex. This business of holding girls back with one hand while pushing them ahead with the other has simply got them in another contradiction. Many of them solve it by accepting intercourse.

Fourth, most girls experience strong social pressures which tend to hurry them into and through the steps leading to marriage. In going through these steps many girls lose their virginity or swap it, hopefully, in an effort to get a permanent relationship. The use of sex as a lure was clearly revealed in my study on premarital intercourse. Many boys reported that very shortly after entering intercourse their partners started talking about possible marriage. As the relationship continued they found that the girls were becoming quite possessive. Plans for marriage were discussed more freely. More and more the girls took marriage for granted, until the boys became convinced that one of the motives for the girls' having intercourse was to bind them to the relationship.

HOW TO HELP GIRLS ESTABLISH SEX STANDARDS

How can girls be helped to deal with the new and complex problems they face? How can they be helped in deciding on sex standards?

First, girls need to be given information about sexual matters, as nearly full and complete information as it is possible to give them. Usually just the opposite view is taken. Parents and other adults have generally tried to keep girls chaste by keeping them in ignorance. They pretend that sex doesn't exist, and hope that the girls remain ignorant of it too, until marriage. In doing this they increase the girls' difficulties and make their problems even less solvable.

My knowledge of masculine psychology leads me to believe that if a girl wishes to preserve her virginity, then knowledge—both general and detailed—is her best safeguard. Many boys have said that the girl "who doesn't know what the score is" is the easiest to persuade. As one boy put it: "A girl who is really ignorant often lets a fellow go so far before she knows what's happening that she can't stop him." An illustration of this came from a sexually experienced boy who had been dating a girl for quite some time. He had made no sexual advances to this girl, however. When asked why, he replied, "I would never have tried anything with that girl. She knew too much. She was a doctor's daughter."

Second, boys need to understand the girl's problem. They also need to be educated to accept their share of the responsibility for what happens in a relationship. It seems unfair for the whole burden to rest upon the girl. Girls, too, feel that this is unfair and illogical. Many of them resent it, and feel that boys should be regarded as equally responsible. One girl, in protesting the unfairness of boys expecting girls to draw the line, said, "Let the boy say when to stop. He knows how excited he is. I don't."

Actually most boys are not as pressing or as heedless of girls as we are sometimes led to think. I am convinced that any girl of reasonably firm character could preserve her virginity quite easily. This assumes that is what she wishes to do. Girls should feel that boys will respect and appreciate a girl who knows her own mind. Then, if she wishes to retain her virginity she should know why. She must be convinced that this is what she wants to do. And then she must make a plain, simple statement concerning her wishes at the appropriate time.

There is a common reason for the failure of girls to do this. It is that the girl wants to maintain the relationship so badly she will not say anything. She fears if she rebuffs the boy's sexual advances she will lose him altogether. Therefore, she says nothing until intercourse is so close she can hardly halt it. This fear of losing the boy also makes her statement of her position unconvincing.

Third, as a part of this information girls need a very clear understanding concerning the place of sex in relationships, and their own sexual nature. For example, when it comes to sex in a relationship, the girl has several pressing questions: If I have intercourse, will it make my relationship with the boy stronger? What will he think of me? Will I please him, or will I lose his respect?

She may read, and she frequently hears, arguments on both sides of these questions. Without anyone to whom she can really talk, and in the absence of convincing information, no wonder she is perplexed. Under these circumstances, when she meets a situation in which she has to say "yes" or "no" to sexual advances, she is unsure and wavering. She is in a frame of mind to accept any point of view that sounds convincing.

This is, of course, another way of saying that girls need both general and detailed information about sex. This seems the best way of assisting girls, for we are certainly living in a time when the sexual standards they follow are very much up to them.

20

What Males Lose by the Double Standard

by LESTER A. KIRKENDALL, PH.D.

Our society has long accepted a double standard in sexual conduct. Under this double standard the female who engages in intercourse outside of marriage is more sharply criticized and more often assumed to be at fault than the male who is her partner. A very common and widespread opinion is that girls suffer more than boys from this double standard. What people don't realize is that boys too experience serious disadvantages in the operation of this double sex standard.

Because women have been (and still are) criticized much more severely than men for engaging in out-of-wedlock intercourse, young women are naturally more hesitant than young men about entering such a relationship. Sexual intercourse is supposed to bring pleasure. In this respect women more than men seem to suffer most. The man is freer to find and enjoy sexual pleasures, we think, and therefore doesn't suffer from the double standard.

WAYS IN WHICH YOUNG MEN SUFFER FROM THE DOUBLE STANDARD

This is the typical way of looking at it, but it is a one-sided one. Actually there are at least three ways in which the young man can run into problems as a result of following the double standard of sex conduct.

The first is that he actually trains himself to be a liar through the kind of approach he makes to women. A young woman, in his thinking, is looked upon with contempt if she accepts his advances. Before intercourse the young man who holds this point of view must conceal his real opinion from his intended sex partner. So that rather than being a real partner, the female becomes the prey which the male hunts and traps into a sex relationship. His success can be achieved only through falsehood. A man could not possibly urge a woman to have intercourse, and at the same time tell her that if she does he will lose his respect for her.

Whether a girl will resist sexual advances has been made the test, by some men, of her possible virtues as a wife. This test, too, would have to be made dishonestly. A young man could never say, "I am inviting you to have intercourse with me. If you accept, I will know that you lack the virtue I want in a wife." Under those circumstances no girl could be expected to accept.

What the male must do, if the girl hesitates, is to cover up his real views with some argument like, "We say we are in love. If we really are, then it is all right." Under these circumstances a warmly affectionate, trusting girl might accept. And because acceptance demonstrates poor character to him, such a man might have lost the very girl who could make him a good wife.

From the male's point of view, then, each double-standard sexual experience in which he engages is, for him, a triumph through deceit. Rather than considering the needs and feelings of another human being, and being straightforward and honest, he has really connived and cheated. Rather than having an equal standing, the girl has in a very real sense been hunted and bagged. The man's objective in these circumstances is to be smooth enough and deceptive enough to capture the girl.

If the girl is aware of how men may think under the double standard, then she, too, becomes unsure of the situation. She is uneasy and suspicious, unable to be really frank or trusting. In such circumstances both are aware that the situation is full of unknown risks, but neither can speak about it to the other. Possibly they may be unwilling to acknowledge the real state of affairs to themselves. Furthermore, a smart and equally scheming girl will be as selfish in her motives as the boy, and as ready to take advantage. Then it becomes a question of who takes advantage of whom. Each may be defeated at his own game, for it is doubtful if, in such an approach to love, anyone can win.

Plenty of evidence suggests that competition and deceit of this sort unfits both men and women for an even-Steven, partner-like sexual relationship in marriage. Looking at the man particularly, as he enters marriage he has failed in his early sex experiences to learn the language, the acts, or the feelings of a real sexual partnership.

Young men are prone to argue that a girl cannot deny all her sexual feelings before marriage and then on the wedding night experience a complete aboutface. By the same logic, neither can a man lure and deceive prior to marriage and then on the wedding night do a comple turnabout. For him to shift suddenly to being an open, fully cooperative, and honest sexual partner is expecting more than is reasonable, just as it is expecting more than is reasonable for the girl to make such a sudden and complete shift.

A second possible consequence of the male's participation in double-standard sexual intercourse is that it is likely to cost him his faith in and respect for women. He is likely to find himself developing a frame of mind in which he says, "You can't trust any woman." This is, of course, a point of view which almost certainly has serious consequences for the marriage relationship. This is especially likely to happen with men who are very successful in their seduction efforts. They are, in effect, slickers who succeed in playing all their victims for "suckers," and in the long run end up thinking that everyone can be fooled. Or, as they say, that any woman can be "made."

Such a double-standard male may feel guilt over his sexual activities. He may then take this guilt out on his partners—his girl friend or spouse. I remember a married soldier I worked with. While overseas he had had numerous sexual partners. He felt unfaithful and disloyal to his wife and had decided upon his return home to confess these experiences to her. I saw him two days after his return. His wife had met his ship and after his discharge they had gone to a hotel together. Before he could unburden himself of his guilt, she confessed to him that she had been unfaithful while he was overseas. He became terribly angry and upset with this confession. He said nothing about his own conduct, but berated his wife for infidelity. He then came to my office to discuss the desirability of divorcing a woman who had been so unfaithful.

In one very exaggerated double-standard situation, I talked with a young man who was bitterly angry with his wife because she had engaged in intercourse with his best friend. During the husband's prolonged absence from home this friend frequently visited the wife. After a time they engaged in intercourse by mutual consent. Later, when the husband returned, the friend very virtuously informed the husband that his wife had "stepped out" on him, and that he knew because he had been her partner. Both men assumed that it was the wife's responsibility to have resisted the advances. Wasn't it natural for a man to take advantage of any sexual opportunity which came along?

Feelings of guilt and suspicion arising from double-standard experience often result in excessive jealousy between the double-standard man and his girlfriend, or his wife.

The third way in which the double standard works to the disadvantage of the man comes when he has children of his own. As his own children become teen-agers, he becomes aware of the children's sex problems. Here again the old suspicions and lack of trust are likely to catch up with him. If he has daughters, memories of his own youth and his seductive activities tend to return as the daughters begin dating. At this point he is likely to become very strict and unyielding with reference to the hours they keep and the places they go, and quite suspicious of the boys they date.

He may be so suspicious and so strict that his daughters rebel and defy him either openly or secretly. His trouble is sometimes sensed by others, for example, the boys who date his daughters. One boy in such a dating situation, in describing the extremely strict dating rules which the father had established for his daughters, said, "Boy, what a life that guy must have led when he was a kid!" This boy was probably a pretty good psychologist.

Another father actually went back to his early experiences when he ordered a boy to cease dating his daughter. When asked the reason for this order by the boy, the father said: "I was young once myself, trying to make every girl I went out with. Just you get out and stay out." A double-standard father may also find it hard to give sex education to his children, particularly when he has to discuss sex problems in dating. To discuss these problems is almost sure to arouse memories of his own experiences. They may be memories he would now prefer to forget, and so, rather than bring them to mind, he says nothing. There is the added difficulty of being in the position of preaching a course of action to his children which he did not follow himself.

Don't let anyone tell you that the double-standard male escapes scot-free from the consequences of his double-standard activities. It just isn't so.

21

Understanding the Problems of the Male Virgin

by LESTER A. KIRKENDALL, PH.D.

Premarital intercourse is widely regarded as a problem in our society, and those youths who engage in it are likely to be considered as being problems or having them. Practically no attention, however, has been given to the feelings, attitudes, and experiences of those *who have refrained* from premarital intercourse. Virginal males are the forgotten youth of our society. Since they are observing conventional standards, they are regarded as neither being nor having sexual problems. Even the word "virgin" itself makes people automatically think only of girls—though it applies equally to boys.

In our split-personality society, we emphasize the desirability of virginity, but at the same time—through movies, jokes, literature, television, and the radio—we make clandestine sex pleasures seem highly desirable. "Sex is something to play at," we say, "but beware of the real thing." Or we seem to say, "Have fun, but don't get caught."

HOW VIRGIN BOYS FEEL

What are the feelings and attitudes of virgin boys toward themselves? What problems do they face? Some of the answers to these questions can be gotten from information that I have gathered in the past few years from virgin boys in interviews and from written statements.

How they feel varies according to whether they are virgins by choice or chance. Even those who were virgins by choice were quite often dissatisfied with their situation. They made such comments as these: "You wonder a lot of times if you're really normal." "You feel as though you're losing out on something." "You feel a little embarrassed or ashamed about it sometimes."

Clues to the virgin boy's feelings are found in the words he chooses as he talks about himself: "Unless I have to, I say nothing about my sexual behavior." "You wonder whether you're missing something." "Sure, I'll admit I'm a virgin." "You feel as though you ought to be getting some experience." He practically never says: "I'm proud of my sexual behavior," or "Sure, I tell them I'm a virgin," or "I'm gaining something."

Most virgin boys dislike being in "bull sessions" in which their male friends get to comparing notes on sexual experiences. In such a situation, the virgin boy is almost always on the defensive. A few will say they are sexually inexperienced if asked directly; otherwise they try to keep that fact under cover. Many adopt the tactic of silent withdrawal. "I just sit back and listen." "I try to sit a little back to the outside of the group. You aren't so easily seen there, and are less likely to be asked a direct question."

Others may manufacture a story. "I can tell as good a story as the next one." "I figure that half the others are lying, so why shouldn't I get in the game. After all, you do want to be one of the group." Still others have found how to maintain a mysterious silence, or to smile knowingly at the "right time," thus leaving the impression that their knowledge is very comprehensive. "I've found just a faint, knowing glance or wink at the right time gets you the reputation of being 'a pretty sly fox,' " said one boy.

Sometimes, depending on the general status of the virgin boy, he may have to withstand considerable ribbing. He will be given suggestions that he get some experience. Friends will offer to help "fix him up," and imply that if he really has "what it takes," he won't remain in the virgin class long. The virgin who doesn't have to face this is usually the one who has attained real standing in his group as an athlete, or is one of its outstanding leaders, or is one who possesses a talent prized by the rest. "The boys found I was a virgin after I had been elected captain," one boy told me. "They never made anything out of it. They seemed to accept it as my choice and let it go at that. I got off better than a lot of other guys, though. Some of them really took a beating." A few have enough self-assurance and conviction so that they are not bothered by the comments of others. "Let 'em talk; I know what I want and that's enough."

One point at which some virgin boys experience rough treatment is in their associations with older men. This is particularly true when boys do summer work with all-male groups, for example, in factories, mills, on the docks, and with road gangs. These older men often make it "pretty rough." "They make you feel there is something wrong if you aren't trying to see how much sex you can get," said one boy. "I worked on a road crew last summer," another told me. "All I heard all summer long was 'Why don't you try it, son. You don't know what you're missing.' "

Another circumstance which indicates how some boys have regarded their inexperience is to ask how they felt after their first experience in intercourse. They often indicate that they looked upon it with a sense of real achievement: "I felt I was right up there along with the other fellows." "I felt I now had something to talk about." And often the experience is used to regale friends! Gaining sexual experience, for some, pretty clearly means masculinity and maturity.

Virgin boys who enter the military services are likely to be bombarded by arguments spurring them on to sexual experience. Away from the associations which usually stabilize them—home, friends, church—they are particularly vulnerable. They find themselves in an environment in which the values they have commonly held may not be held or understood by others.

More than anything else these boys need to understand clearly the reasons for the pattern they have chosen. They are often unable to voice any reasons, or to voice them clearly, or to defend them if they are attacked. Basically, many boys remain virgins because they cling to a feeling that fair play must underlie good relationships. They feel that somehow virginity is a matter of fairness, but ordinarily they cannot make it clear just how. There has never been any frank, straightforward discussion to clarify issues or to help the virgin boy marshal his thoughts. Some boys find help through reading. Help of this sort is particularly needed in the middle or late teens, but as one fellow said: "Try to get it."

Is there something positive to be gained by abstaining from or participating in premarital intercourse? The average boy would like to know, and to know what it is, but the average parent or teacher either can't or won't tell him. Many adults will try to answer this challenge by saying: "You'll never be able to live with yourself," or "You'll never regret it." These comments are vague and intangible ("glittering generalities" one fellow called them), and give little help to the virgin boy who is seeking something positive and strong on which to base his standards.

The average boy can get, so far as authoritative sources are concerned, only vague, unsatisfying references to things about the place of sex in life. One boy commented on a parental teaching which was evidently directed toward keeping him a virgin. His parents had said only this (but many times): "Treat every girl as you would your sister." His comment was: "But girls don't want me to treat them as I treat my sister (and it's not that I mistreat her), and I don't want to treat them this way. I have a different feeling for the girls I date, yet I want to respect them. I'd like to know how sex fits into dating and the various consequences and outcomes resulting from using sex and affection in different ways."

An even greater degree of mystery surrounds the sex act itself, and here curiosity becomes a real problem for some! As one boy put it: "You always almost see them do it in the movies, but never quite do." One boy who had been looking for objective information concerning the nature of intercourse had been frustrated at every turn. There was "nothing, not a darn thing" in his school library or in his schoolbooks. The public library had some materials under lock and key and labeled "For Adults Only." This five-foot eight-inch sixteen-year-old stripling was clearly not "adult," at least not when fixed by the gimlet glare of the head librarian. He was reduced then to a red-faced, stammering incoherence. Frustrated on every hand, he exploded angrily: "It's a great note. You can't do and you can't know."

Not until his vexed and baffled outburst did I clearly realize the double demand placed on most of these virgin boys, particularly when they are in their teens. Not only do we say, "Hold your impulses in check," but we add, "do it in ignorance." It leads to the question one boy asked: "What percentage is there in remaining virgin?" The virgin boy feels the need for support in his pattern of behavior. He very seldom gets it from the people who are most likely to demand that pattern from him—his parents, his teachers, his religious leaders. Over and over, when I have asked the question "Do your parents (or teachers) know you are a virgin?" the answer is "No."

These circumstances belie the common statement that it is sordid and licentious discussions of sex which distress adults. Here is a chance to discuss and commend a pattern of behavior that presumably is wholesome and commendable. Yet nothing is said about it. "They just don't want to talk about sex, period," is the way one boy summed it up.

SOURCES OF SUPPORT FOR VIRGIN BOYS

Some virgin boys can get support, however. Usually it is from a close friend who like himself has decided to remain chaste. These two support each other, and in their mutual understanding they find a strength which enables them to disregard counter pressures. One boy told me: "Jim, my best friend, and I agreed that we thought it better to remain virgins. We have talked it over a lot of times and stuck right together on it. Even when other of our friends went ahead, it never bothered us."

Other boys have found their support from girl friends with whom they have discussed standards: "My girl said she really appreciated my attitude and that helped matters a lot." It doesn't always turn out that way, though. One fellow, when he tried to discuss the subject of male virginity with his girl friend, got a sharp rebuff: "She said: 'Well, that is a new line.' I guess she thought I was trying to 'make out' with her by coming at it from an entirely new direction."

Two sources of support for these boys should be noted. The first is discussion that gives them a clear insight into the meaning and reason for the standards they are asked to hold. The second is identification with parents or other adults whom the boy admires and who exemplify the standards he is trying to follow.

Standards of sexual behavior—and this appears to be as true of promiscuity as it is of virginity—are much less a matter of sexual knowledge than of feelings—feelings of acceptance or rejection, of accomplishment or failure. Few persons form their sexual standards as a result of facts and information—the traditional sex education. Rather their standards are a product of the kind of relationships they have developed with their parents and close friends.

If you want to help your son (or other youth) in coping with the problems of an age which overrates sex, there are several things you can do:

(1) *Discuss sexual standards openly.* Discussions should be in the detail needed to help the boy understand the place of sex in life and the reasons for standards. Vague, evasive discussions only raise questions and stir conflict. Standards cannot be imposed. They need to be based on an approach to human relations (for example, what is fair) that appeals to youth as positive and rational.

(2) *Recognize frankly that virginity in and of itself is not the real issue.* The issue is not whether a youth is experienced or inexperienced. The central concern should be teaching how to use sex positively. Exploitive, self-centered, injurious use of sex as contrasted to a meaningful and dignified use is the core of the problem, and we stray from the point by concentrating on the individual's state of virginity or nonvirginity. Under conditions in which the rights and welfare of others can be safeguarded, each person has the right to look forward to sexual relationships. What

needs to be discussed and understood is what circumstances are needed to ensure the proper safeguards, and approval given to conduct that genuinely shows concern for others and their welfare.

(3) *Get over your own fears of and inhibitions about sex.* Center your emphasis on the positive contributions that sex can make in a good relationship between husband and wife.

(4) *Don't try to protect a youth against all temptation.* This can't be done anyway. Instead, strengthen him by giving him insight, support, and appreciation.

(5) *Make the youth a respected and integral member of your family, and help him get the same feeling of membership in the community itself.* There is today too much separation of youth and adults into separate and isolated social groups. If the youth feels that he can attain a status of respect and maturity in other ways, he may be less impelled to engage in sex experience just in order to prove to himself and his friends that he is grown up and mature.

22

The Relationship Between Sex and Love

by LESTER A. KIRKENDALL, PH.D.

"What is the relationship between sex and love?" is a common question of teen-agers. It is usually raised by someone who is trying to understand himself, his feelings and his sexual desires. The customary answer to this question is confusing and contradictory. Teen-agers are ordinarily told that, even though they have much affection for each other, there should be no sexual feelings between them, since they are unmarried. Or they are made to feel that, if there are any sexual desires, they are wrong. Certainly if there are any, according to this view, they will be wholly and carefully held back. After marriage, sex then blossoms forth and becomes a beautiful and sacred expression of full and complete love.

This view reflects a very narrow and shallow concept of sex. It lacks the depth necessary if sex is to contribute as much as it might to a permanent love relationship. It focuses attention on the physical expression of sex, and generally regards sex as being intercourse and nothing else. The supposed lack of a tie between sex and premarital love appear illogical. The reason, of course, is that this view is designed to enforce the standard of premarital chastity, not to explain the physical expression of love.

THE RELATIONSHIP BETWEEN PHYSICAL NEARNESS AND LOVE

Let's forget this view and start fresh. Let's start by thinking of the relationship of physical nearness, of touch, of embracing, of close body contact to affection and love. Everyone knows that in relationships where there is affection there is also a desire to touch, to hug, to bring bodies closely together in physical contact. This holds true in all relationships throughout life, for all ages, and in both male-female, male-male, and female-female relationships. The mother comforts her baby by embracing and patting it. A hurt finger is made less painful with a kiss. A person long separated from his family or friends is greeted upon his return by hugs and embraces.

Physical nearness, then, is a means of saying something of importance. We comfort by touching and hugging; likewise we express our pleasure and affection through body contact. I recall when my children were small that, as I picked one of them up for an embrace, the child was likely to say: "Squeeze me tight, Daddy." I have experimented by squeezing him so tightly that I supposed it must be uncomfortable. Still I have had the child say: "Squeeze me tighter, Daddy."

This wish to touch in the expression of affection is common to both sexes. In our culture, however, and others as well, there are differences in the acceptable ways for male and female, and for different ages to express these feelings. In America, women can express these feelings to other women more freely and openly than men can express them to other men. Kissing and embracing among women may be regarded with some amusement, even disdain, especially by men, but still they are socially acceptable.

Men also feel affection for each other, and experience the same impulse to touch and embrace as do women. Such feelings if openly displayed in our society would be disapproved and regarded as unmanly. So men get around it by pounding each other on the back and swearing affectionately. The deeper their affection, the harder they hit and the louder they swear. Who has not seen adolescent boys after a victorious football or basketball game embrace each other, and pound one another on the back?

Also, as children reach the age of sexual maturity, fear of the sex drive and the strong disapproval of premarital sexual intercourse causes many adults to disapprove of any expression of feeling among adolescents through physical contact. It generally seems quite satisfactory, even desirable for Johnny to comfort Susan by putting his arms around her, by embracing her, when they are in kindergarten. But physical closeness when they come to the junior high school seems full of danger.

This is the age when teachers and principals are upset by hand-holding in classes or by couples who walk down the corridor arm in arm. What seemed good and desirable at five or six years of age, because of our fear of sex seems full of threat and danger at fifteen or sixteen. And, of course, it is true that these adolescent expressions are tied with sexual feelings and may quite easily be extended to direct sexual experience including intercourse.

So we must say that with affection comes always the desire to touch, to caress, to come close physically. In the male-female love relationship, sexual intercourse becomes the most intimate and the closest of all touch relationships. It becomes the ultimate in meaning—in joy, in giving, in receiving, in fun and enjoyment. This is its fullest realization.

Sex to be realized in this way needs to be related to love by honest and responsible expression. That is, the partners must desire to use their sexual capacities to express their real feelings to each other. They must also know *how* to express themselves this way, for it does not come simply from desire. They cannot, for example, use sex in a deceptive way, for strictly self-centered purposes, nor in a way that would cause injury or hurt to either partner. It must be recognized, of course, that sex can be and is often used without love or affection.

The desire to touch, to come close, and for sexual expression is coupled with affection in the male-female relationship. If persons in love could not have these feelings, we would properly be worried about them. Seen in this setting, the argument "If you loved me, you would have intercourse with me" becomes an argument of personal pride or desire, rather than of love. It is like saying, "If you loved me, you would touch me." Logically this is true. If there were love the desire to touch would be there. However, to argue that if one does touch, this is proof of love is foolish. And the same is true of intercourse.

There are problems, then, for both youth and for older persons. For young people in love, it is how to express their feelings of affection in an honest and responsible fashion. They need to learn how to speak to one another honestly about their feelings of affection and to set sex in a much broader framework than it is commonly set.

Adults have the more difficult task. Many of them have the problem of overcoming many years of misteaching. They have deep-seated feelings of fear and disgust concerning sex. They regard it simply as a physical, sensual experience which is always threatening to overpower judgment and due regard for others. They judge morality in terms of the presence or absence of sexual experience. For many adults the need is first to unlearn, then to build a concept of sex on a new and a broader foundation. As they do this, they can see sex in a different light, recognize its place in living, and understand that its expression can be guided and directed.

Part VII

*Understanding the Problems
Involved in Premarital Sex*

23

What I Would Tell My Daughter About Premarital Sex

by JAMES LESLIE McCARY, PH.D.

As a part of the course in Marriage and Family Life which I teach at the University of Houston, students ask frank questions about sex and receive equally frank and direct answers. One question that is asked each semester is, "What would you tell your daughter about premarital sex?" My answer was recorded by one of the students and a written transcript is presented here as one view which parents might consider when giving sex information and training to their children.

This question about one's daughter, I tell my students, is often received by psychologists who talk on problems of sex. Most often it is meant to embarrass the psychologist, the questioner assuming that the psychologist will talk out of both sides of his mouth; that is, he might make certain liberal statements about sexual matters to the public, but when it comes to his own daughter he will forget his academic views and become as rigid, as demanding, as moralistic as the next father.

The question "What would you tell your daughter about premarital sex?" is one that cannot be answered with one short statement because a whole lifetime of living sets the stage for the answer. But let me at least give you some of my own thinking and views on the question. I will assume questioners mean a daughter who is roughly of their age—that is college level.

I would want my daughter to know the biological and physiological sexual structure of the male and of the female and I'd want her to understand thoroughly the similarities and differences between these two sexes. I'd want her to know not only the biological and physiological makeup but the psychological makeup. I'd want her to know that males, for example, are made more easily sexually excited than are females and are made easily excited by different methods and different techniques than are females. I'd want her to know what these techniques are so she might avoid their use in many situations, but, also, so she could make use of them in appropriate situations.

I'd want consistency in all matters if possible, but certainly I would want consistency in sexual matters in the home. I think that a parent has to be consistent within himself in order to produce sane and predictable ideas in the daughter; a parent must feel at ease with his sexual ideas if he is to present the same attitude and approach to sex day in and day out. He should come to his own conclusions as to what is proper before he makes a statement or shows his attitude which his children are to adopt.

I furthermore would wish that both parents would be consistent between themselves; that is, that the mother and the father would have consistent ideas about sex—that the father should not make certain demands and present one set of ideas while the mother makes different demands and presents a different set of ideas. Inconsistency can only produce confusion and insecurity within the child. If a child accepts the ideas of the father, frequently he feels guilty about not accepting the ideas of the mother, and on the other hand, if he accepts the ideas of the mother, he feels guilty about rejecting the ideas of the father. The child has to learn to depend upon one set of rules and regulations, not a new set with each parent.

Equally important with these first two points covering consistency is the fact that the home should be somewhat consistent with the outside world. Now, this certainly cannot always be done in sexual matters because society is too varied in the demands it makes and what it expects of its members, depending upon what subculture and area one encounters. Therefore, I would want my daughter to understand that there will be some inconsistencies in society's expectations with what she is taught in our home and that she must understand what it is that society expects and demands. She must understand the attitudes of bigots, the people whom Dr.

Albert Ellis has called the sexual fascists; she must understand that these people disagree with any person who does not conform to their way of thinking, demanding and behaving, and that they are ready to condemn and even persecute those who do not follow to the letter their unbending ideas.

I'd want her to know of methods and techniques of sexual outlet other than sexual intercourse, and I'd want her to know the values of these methods. I would want her to know that masturbation and petting are perfectly normal modes of behavior that can and will satisfy sexual urges and that at the same time do not carry with them some of the same problems that are found resulting from sexual intercourse.

I would want my daughter—and my son, too, for that matter—to have a kind and fair attitude toward her fellow man. I'd want her to be fair and ethical in all relationships, including sex. There should be no cheating, no lying, no taking advantage of others. I'd want her to understand that when her behavior in any way harms another person or harms herself, that this is behavior which should be reconsidered because it is oftentimes behavior which is truly evil.

I'd want her to understand that sex is a game for many boys and young men, and that she must be prepared for lies and trickery. Seduction is an ego boost for boys and for men who feel sexually inferior. She must understand how boys get this attitude from a society which has a disturbed attitude toward sex, and that this behavior is not a personal thing directed toward her. For these boys and emotionally disturbed men, seduction is an act that is designed to increase, albeit only momentarily, their ego strength, and they are not necessarily after sex as such. When she finds men behaving in such a manner, she must understand that this is their problem and deal with it accordingly.

I'd want her to understand the views of various religions and to understand how the unwise use of some of the ideas and ideals from these religions can produce guilt and repressions. I'd furthermore want her to understand guilt and repression, and if she avoids sex to do so because of rational factors and not guilt, because guilt in this area, as well as in others, leads to many problems, and sexual conflicts resulting from guilt can be devastating.

If, with all this information, along with the attitude and background of her home, she still decided on sexual intercourse, then I would want her to certainly know about and have access to contraceptive devices. This would include information on pregnancy and venereal diseases, which, incidentally should be made available to all children at an early age.

I'd want her to know that, basically, I think one is usually significantly better off if he or she avoids premarital sexual intercourse, especially if in the teens, and would, in most cases, be better off to use masturbation or petting when sexual expression is necessary. But, if she makes the other decision, that is, to have sexual intercourse before marriage, I would want her to know that, while I might think she has made a foolish mistake, no matter what she does along these lines, so long as she does not hurt herself or others, I am with her and my respect and love will not change. And I would hope, and I believe it would follow, that, if she ever needed a friend, that she would turn first to her father and/or mother and know that she would receive support from either of us.

These are the principles in which I believe and are the ones by which I raised my daughter who is now happily married. I do not know whether or not she had premarital sexual intercourse—and frankly, I couldn't care less; I respect her and love her too much even to question her, although I could ask and she could answer without embarrassment to either of us. I am pleased that she has an open and healthy attitude toward sex and that she does not have the guilt or shame or fear which causes sexual repressions which can later build to such an intense peak that they erupt into sexual or neurotic acting out. Because of her views on sex—among other things—she is likely to remain emotionally stable and healthy.

24

How Premarital Sex May Hurt Girls

by LESTER A. KIRKENDALL, PH.D.

Girls are usually quite unaware and ignorant of how boys feel about sex. They often understand how to lure boys, but not how boys feel toward those who lure them. Thus a girl knows that a boy is attracted to her when she has aroused him sexually. But they expect different outcomes from the ones they get. The girl hopes that this attraction is the beginning of affection and a dating relationship; the boy generally anticipates the pleasures of intercourse, and seeks the opportunity which may provide it. This kind of attraction is not the affection for which the girl hopes, however.

The sexual luring is often carried on into complete intercourse, but under circumstances which create in the boy feelings of disrespect for the girl. This is so contrary to what the girl wanted—or hoped for—that she is naturally hurt when she finds out about it. She had hoped for affection and attachment; what she got was contempt and abandonment. *Who wouldn't be hurt?*

Girls are pressured and pushed by friends, relations, and public opinion to date, to find a boyfriend, to get engaged. *And hurry up about it!* At the same time they have less chance to ask for dates and to decide whom to date than boys have. Each girl in a very real sense is in competition with all of her friends for the attention of boys. These pressures make many girls emotionally upset, uneasy, and insecure. They are not able to take disappointment easily. They can't look at a shaky or broken relationship objectively. They are often, in other words, in a state of mind and feeling which makes them "fall in love" quickly and easily. It also makes it very easy for them to be hurt.

When emotionally upset a girl often trusts unwisely. Had she not been in such a hurry she would have been better able to know when to trust and when not to. It is so easy for a girl to believe a boy when he says "I love you," because this is what she wants so badly to believe. When the boy argues that intercourse will increase his love, this is easy to believe, too, for again this is what she wants to happen. When it turns out that she trusted too easily, or hoped for too much, feeling hurt is a normal reaction.

One must remember, too, that the girl's unrealistic trusting is not always the fault of the boy. The boy may have been perfectly honest and sincere, but the girl may still fool herself into believing what she wants to believe. And so the pressures and insecurities which girls have lead them into immature, unstable situations, and about the only outcome possible is "hurt."

Once intercourse has taken place, a girl is likely to feel insecure and uneasy. If pregnancy or discovery occurs, what support would she have? It is natural enough for her to become frightened and jittery. As a result girls frequently press so hard to make the dating relationship secure that they produce a "fight-back" reaction on the part of the boy.

There are usually two possible results when one of the persons in a relationship feels pressed to move faster than he wants. One is for him to break off the relationship. The other is for him to take advantage of the other person. And so when the girl begins to urge the boy to commit himself, he is likely to draw away, sometimes angrily. He may break the relationship in such a way that the girl never understands exactly what has happened. Or the boy may feel that the girl, in pressuring him, is taking advantage of him. He responds by taking advantage of her. If intercourse has not occurred, he may use her urgency as an excuse for getting it started. As one boy put it: "I knew when she began pushing me to get engaged that I could get whatever I wanted. I decided I might just as well get some sex out of it."

Girls are hurt by public opinion much more than boys when something goes wrong with the sex relationship. If she gets pregnant, or if she is found out in some other way, the girl is judged more harshly. This punishment is often severe enough to hurt many girls quite badly. They may feel they are being criticized unfairly, or that the double standard of sex morality which causes them to be blamed more severely than boys is just plain wrong. If the boy leaves the girl to face her problems alone, she is likely to feel doubly hurt.

Girls mature earlier than boys. This difference is most pronounced in the high-school years. This means that girls in the early and middle teens are ordinarily more ready for loyalty and permanence in relationships than boys their own age. They invest their time and give their loyalty to a boy, and expect the same from him. They are unaware that his first loyalty is likely to be to his close boyfriends—to his gang—rather than to a girl. If sexual intercourse occurs, he is much more likely to tell his friends about it than the girl is apt to tell her friends. If they break off, the girl is likely to find that their sex relationship is common knowledge among his boyfriends. *In fact, she is likely to find these boys dating her in hopes of obtaining intercourse.*

Girls may get hurt because the experience in intercourse has a different meaning for a girl than it has for a boy. She is conditioned more than the boy to want expressions of tenderness and sentimental feeling. Thus the girl will feel, because she is taught to want these feelings, that the closeness of intercourse means love, affection, and permanence in the relationship. She is likely, unless she knows the way boys think, to feel even in a new relationship that the boy wants intercourse because he cares for her as a person. The boy, however, is much more likely to think of sex as an evidence of masculine achievement, or in terms of the pleasure he can gain from it. As a matter of fact, it is common for boys and young men to refer to the achievement of intercourse with a girl as "scoring," or "making a score."

The differences in view are especially likely to exist in a relationship which has been in existence for only a short time. As the relationship strengthens and affection develops, the boy in particular is less likely to strive for sex as a physical or purely pleasure experience. One thing is certain—as male and female they are not likely to look at sex in the same way. And so out of their different ideas and concepts about sex may come hurt and disillusionment for the girl—and disrespect on the part of the boy.

25

Why Boys "Lose Respect"

by LESTER A. KIRKENDALL, PH.D.

"After that I lost all respect for her." This is a common reaction on the part of boys after they have had premarital intercourse with a girl. "Loss of respect" is a loose term, to say the least. As boys use it it may mean almost any unfavorable change in feeling. The phrase is so commonly used, in fact, that loss of respect is often thought to be an *inevitable result* of premarital intercourse. This is not so. What then are the real reasons behind this so-called loss of respect? I have discussed the matter with both young men and young women. The following explanations resulted.

(1) The boy actually never respected the girl *before* sexual intercourse occurred. He may fail to recognize what his feelings actually are, and he will often deny this disrespect, even to himself. Self-deception comes easily in his eagerness for sexual intercourse. Once the novelty and excitement of the physical act wears off, his real feelings come to the surface.

If before intercourse the boy can cover up his contempt, he can go ahead without feeling too guilty. He may feel that having intercourse is wrong, but having it with a girl one has no use for is even worse. So he refuses to recognize what he actually feels. Boys who do not believe in the double standard are likely to feel guilty about having intercourse with girls they don't respect; "double-standard boys" usually find it easier to have intercourse with girls for whom they feel no respect.

(2) Sometimes disrespect is produced by lewd, coarse jests made by close male friends of the boy involved. Boys often regard sexual experience as evidence that they have reached manhood. This being so, they feel the need to tell other boys about it. Even though the boy and girl may have respected each other, and behaved in a dignified way, boyfriends are unlikely to treat their relationship that way. They are likely to see it as a salacious, exciting lark. It becomes very difficult for the boy to maintain his feelings of dignity when close friends begin to refer to his relationship with the girl in coarse, vulgar language.

Even though the boy opened the way for such comments from his friends by telling them about his relationship, he may still find his feelings changed by their remarks. Sometimes the fact that a couple are having intercourse becomes general knowledge among their friends, and the couple know this. The knowledge that others know certainly removes the sense of exclusiveness which the couple probably felt at first. They begin to fear that still others, perhaps their parents, may find out. These fears in turn produce tensions, and out of them often come quarrels and loss of respect between the partners. Unless the partners have a great amount of affection and a strong loyalty to each other, feelings of contempt are likely to build up as a defense against feelings of uneasiness and fear.

(3) Some boys feel that in a secret, hidden sexual relationship the girl should be coy and resisting. She should require seduction on each association. If the girl abandons this role, and becomes enthusiastic, aggressive, or even seductive herself, she may very well be greeted with a feeling of disrespect on the part of her partner.

(4) A girl may lose the respect of her male sexual partner through her use of sex slang or folk terms. As one boy put it: "I just can't stand a girl who is dirty-mouthed." Yet his partner had spoken only in ordinary sexual slang. He himself had used these

terms in talking with the girl. There is a good chance that since he had used them she felt it was correct for her to use them also.

(5) Once intercourse begins, girls often respond by becoming keenly interested in getting engaged or married. Girls involved in premarital intercourse are often quite insecure. To become engaged or to have the promise of marriage would provide a girl much-needed security. So she begins to press for expressions of love, and to force the boy to commit himself. The boy, however, may be quite unready or quite unwilling for such an involvement. As a consequence of this pressure the boy may lose interest in the relationship, find another girl, or for some other reason wish to be free. To "lose respect" for the girl provides him with an excellent excuse for ending the relationship without causing him to feel guilty.

(6) Sometimes when her boyfriend begins to lose interest, the girl senses this. In order to keep him she may behave so as to create a lack of respect. She may have permitted or even encouraged intercourse to begin with as a way of promoting the relationship. She may now reason that, since a stronger relationship did seem to result from intercourse, the way to revive interest is to make intercourse even more available. And so she becomes sexually aggressive. Girls who behave this way are often criticized by the boys because "intercourse got to be all she thought about." It is very easy for a naïve, insecure girl to overplay her hand. It is just as easy for a boy who was never very deeply involved anyway to "lose respect."

(7) Some boys want exclusive possession of their sexual partners. A boy who holds this view may be tortured with the thought, "if she had intercourse with me, she would have it with someone else." The girl herself, by what she says or does, may create and foster this suspicion. A flirtatious, provocative girl can easily do this, and her partner will quite likely respond with a growing feeling of contempt.

(8) Breaking a relationship, particularly one in which there was some affection, is never easy. It is even harder when sexual intercourse has been a part of it. It is especially hard for young people who lack the courage to face reality, who are unskilled in dealing with tangled emotions and who are unable to speak frankly about sex. As a result breaks are often made by roundabout methods and

in dishonest ways. Lies, false fronts, and advantage-taking become a part of making the break. In a situation such as this, to safeguard his own conscience a boy often "loses respect." He is thus able to look back on what he has done with less guilt and disturbance than if he had "respected" the girl.

(9) A "loss of respect" for the girl may be the boy's reaction to a sexual relationship which failed to meet expectations. Inexperienced boys especially, often expect more in pleasure, thrill, and excitement from sex than is possible. The sensory pleasure may be little, the girl may cry or otherwise create a problem, or the back seat of a car may prove an unsuitable place for a sexual relationship. In other words, sex just didn't live up to expectations. Intercourse was supposed to be the most satisfying of all intimacies; instead it produced tensions and hard feelings.

10) Loss of respect may be the to-be-expected outcome of managing sex by ritual. Since young people cannot talk freely about sex, they often conduct their sexual affairs in a stereotyped way. Thus, in petting the boy makes an advance, the girl resists, he tries again and gets a bit further before she stops him. One step leads to another. Both know what comes next, and both know they will end up with petting. The girl may then cry to prove her virtue, and the ritual is completed. In such a relationship, when intercourse finally occurs, the loss of respect by the boy may be as much a part of the ritual as pushing him away and crying is for the girls. *The boy is expected to lose respect and he does.*

Clearly a loss of respect for a girl by a boy who has engaged in premarital intercourse with her may arise from a number of causes. Their very number, however, indicates how hard it is in our double-standard, sexually confused culture to combine premarital intercourse with a pleasant, secure dating relationship. This is especially true when the partners are youthful and immature.

26

A College Student Talks About Sex

by ROBERT J. McDERMOTT

I have read articles in many magazines from time to time discussing the declining morals of American youth and the sexual
misbehavior in which teen-agers engage. My reading has led me to
think that some plain talking by teen-agers who know what is
going on would be helpful. I hope to start the ball rolling. I am an
eighteen-year-old college junior with, I suspect, considerably more
than the average amount of sexual experience for a person my age.
During the last year I have been looking back and thinking about
these experiences. I became interested in doing this because while
I was obtaining intercourse easily and often, I found that I was
actually not gaining the kind of satisfaction I wanted. I was moving
from one girl to another, but finding nothing I really wanted to
stay with in any of the relationships.

I have thought much about what I have learned from these
experiences, and how they have affected me both good and bad.
I believe I have some things to say which would help parents and
others in understanding teen-agers and their sexual experiences.
I have been helped in my thinking by considerable reading concerning sexual behavior, and by numerous discussions with several
adult friends who have been willing to talk frankly, and who have,
I think, good insights into sexual behavior and good common sense
about life.

I have known about, and used, masturbation since I was thirteen
years old. My first experience in intercourse came when I was

fourteen with a girl about my age. Shortly thereafter, a married woman, age twenty-four, living near my home, made herself freely available. She was highly sexed, and sexually sophisticated. She taught me a great deal about various kinds of sexual activity. After about six months she left the community. I then turned to other partners and in the next three years had intercourse with many girls. Some of these relationships lasted for rather long periods of time. These were all either casual acquaintances or pickups. I have never had intercourse with a steady dating partner.

I believe that my sexual association with the married woman had a more important influence on me than any of the other of my experiences. It was actually quite important to me for it helped me prove my masculinity. At that time especially, I needed to feel masculine and sexually attractive. I had a very unsatisfactory father-son relationship. I had no pattern upon which I could base my masculinity. I was small in stature, wore thick, ugly glasses, and looked a lot younger than I really was.

There is, I feel, a basic reason for this wish for intercourse to prove masculinity which operates for most teen-age boys. *The older men I knew felt that boys were not men until they had had sexual intercourse.* Consequently, when a boy finds himself sexually attractive to a girl or woman, he feels as if he is not only grown up, but superior even to older boys who are not having intercourse. I know I began to take notice of my appearance and to drop childish pranks. I think I even started to take a deeper interest in my future and in the world around me.

But at the same time the association caused problems. I grew apart from children my own age. I felt them immature, inexperienced, and complete bores. As I have been outgrowing my need for casual sex, I have found it hard to know how to act with friends my own age. An even more difficult problem arising from this association is that it created a sexual appetite which has been hard for me to handle. I had sex on my mind constantly. I think it was this which led me into the numerous casual experiences I have had.

DIFFICULTIES ARISING FROM TOO-EARLY SEXUAL RELATIONSHIPS

I know of at least two difficulties arising from this type of experience. *One of the most damaging of these is the deceitfulness which surrounds so much of the premarital intercourse—at least the casual kind I have experienced.* The kind of deceitfulness in which I have been involved creates a kind of distrust and a cynical attitude which makes it hard to work with people.

First, the boy deceives the girl by telling her lies, and then he deceives himself by telling lies to himself and to his friends. Many times a boy will tell his friends that a girl was good at intercourse, that winning her was easy, and that the after-effects were sheer delight. Actually, he may have had an unsatisfactory time because the girl may have been inexperienced. Or he himself may have been a poor partner, and the place where intercourse occurred may have been uncomfortable or exposed, as in the back seat of a car. There could be many reasons for an unsatisfactory experience. But most boys try to overlook them, and pretend they never existed.

A point at which deception always occurs is when the boy starts to seduce the girl—or the other way around, for I have had that happen too. I have found in trying to achieve intercourse that the thing I usually needed to do was to give the girl an excuse for going ahead that would make it seem that she had been persuaded.

There are three common ways that boys use to furnish girls excuses for participating in sex. One is to engage in so much stimulating foreplay that the girl can say she was too excited to control herself. Liquor makes it possible to say: "I didn't know what I was doing." Finally there is always the argument that "this is love." These excuses enable them, especially the girls, to go ahead without feeling guilty. The boy usually knows this is deception, and I'm sure that the girl knows it too.

The second difficulty is that you develop an attitude which leads the boy to disregard girls' feelings and needs. A prime example of this occurred when a friend and I picked up two girls off the street. We saw the girls waving and smiling at us, so we stopped and asked them to ride with us. They were in the car before we could finish our invitation. One girl got in the back with my friend; the

other got in the front with me. I had driven for just a few minu
when I stopped the car. We immediately had intercourse with
girls. Neither of us had seen the girls before in our lives. For the
next two months, my friend and I had frequent intercourse with
these girls, as did many other college boys. Some seven or eight
months after we stopped seeing them, both became pregnant. All
the boys laughed and thought it was a great joke.

This situation was a bad one for many reasons. The boys were
having to prove they were *men* to themselves and each other. The
girls were using sex to attract boys, hoping they might establish a
permanent relationship with one of them. All they got was a poor
reputation, heartache, and grief. One of the girls came from a
broken family and the other had a mother in a mental hospital.
Two girls' lives are probably ruined because they and a group of
boys didn't know how to express themselves properly. One thing
which I completely believe, however, is that while these boys were
all laughing outwardly, inwardly they were very sorry and felt like
crying. I know I did.

Many of my sex relations have been with so-called tramps.
These are the ones about which I feel the most regret. Looking
back at these girls, I find that every one of them has had either a
broken home, an unhappy home, an inability to make friends, or
a broken heart over some boy. Such girls are easier to seduce than
girls with happy, stable lives because they can be deceived easier.

My experiences have taught me a lot about the ways in which
males and females think and feel about each other and sex. Believe
it or not, I found I could become fed up or tired with sex. For most
boys, intercourse isn't as good, wonderful, or thrilling as they
thought it would be, but still they will tell each other and themselves that it is. As a result, the boys experiment with sex without
really understanding sex, themselves, or girls. What else but trouble
could result?

So far as the future is concerned I know it is risky to predict,
especially after one has developed such a pattern as I did. Looking
ahead I may have more premarital intercourse, but, if so, under
better circumstances. I would want it with a girl I respect and care
enough for to consider marrying. We should be able to talk freely

about all aspects of our relationship. That way the chances of hurt would be greatly reduced.

As a result of my reflections I want to make some suggestions to parents, teachers, and other adults:

(1) *Get on the ball and do something!* As it is, almost everything is left to the movies. They do nothing but distort sex and life in general. Teen-agers get their ideas about sex from such movies as "Beach Party" or "Come Blow Your Horn" and go out to try to live that way. There is no one to help them correct their ideas. Someone needs to have the courage to talk frankly to them.

(2) *Don't make sex seem so evil.* I have found that sex can be understood and directed. In my own experience, once I had a chance to discuss it frankly and to get a different pattern of life started, things became much easier. I have even found that masturbation, which is so commonly disapproved, releases many of my tensions. Once a person is involved in sexual experiences what he needs is someone to talk over his experiences with. The last thing he needs is someone to yell at him and warn him that he is on the wrong road. He may find this out himself in the process, as I think I have. Just treat sex like any other type of problem.

(3) *Don't be afraid of teen-agers!* They appreciate finding someone they can talk with. Talking with them won't push them into sex activity by making them sexually excited. Actually talking makes sex more understandable and easier to control. The teen-ager needs help in solving his problems, of course, but he is the one who has to solve them. *No one else can do it for him.*

27

Why Teen-Age Boys Visit Prostitutes

by LESTER A. KIRKENDALL, PH.D.

Most parents and teachers probably believe that the days when a middle-class boy "sowed his wild oats" by going to a prostitute have passed. Yet—to judge from the information I gathered from a recent study—they are quite wrong. The study involved two hundred young men, ranging from eighteen to twenty-three years of age. I found that very nearly one fifth of them had had intercourse with a prostitute at least once. Most of these experiences had occurred during their teens.

This group consisted of college-level men. Figures gathered by myself and others (particularly Kinsey) indicate that about half of all men at this educational level have premarital intercourse. This means, if these figures could be applied country-wide, that about 10 per cent of all college-level boys have sexual experience with a prostitute. This is probably a conservative estimate, since the average age of my subjects at the time of the interview was just over twenty and a half years. Kinsey found that by the time his college-level subjects had reached twenty-five years of age—28 per cent of them had had experience with prostitutes.

This figure rises even higher when all teen-age boys are included—not just those who go to college. The earlier boys leave school, according to Kinsey, the larger is the proportion of them who patronize prostitutes. The exact figures are not so important.

What is important is the need to recognize that there are still quite a few teen-age boys who seek sexual experience with prostitutes, and to understand why they do.

Many persons will say that these boys visit prostitutes because of the need for satisfying a strong sex drive. But again this is an incorrect judgment. Actually, "going to a prostitute" for teen-agers is a group experience. The boys participate in it because they need and want to feel grown-up and sophisticated. In the group I studied, "going to a prostitute" usually meant going with one or more friends, or "buddies." The descriptions of what occurred made it clear that this was a kind of group adventure. The occasion was used by the boys to test and challenge each other, and as a method of gaining status among their adolescent friends.

Here are typical descriptions, given by two boys, showing how they and their friends, all of them sexually inexperienced at the time, got to prostitutes. John's first experience, he said, took place after a fraternity initiation. In order to relax, three pledges, close friends, went for a drive. One of them, who had been to a prostitute before, suggested they go some place and have intercourse. The other fellows were receptive. As John recalls it, they nudged and dared each other until all of them were in a position in which they were unable to withdraw without being "considered chicken." John thinks that secretly they wanted it that way. He feels that they were curious, yet none could have gone by himself. "We had to sort of dare each other."

Bill's story was similar. One evening a group of fellows about Bill's age, about fourteen and older, were "fooling" around town. They got to talking about sex, and as a result of the discussion all chipped in enough to raise $5.00 so one of the group might go to one of the local houses and have intercourse with a prostitute. Bill drew the lot, so the fellows took him to the house and waited in the living room for him while he went in for intercourse.

"Going to a house" makes an exciting conversational topic. Of course the fellows who participate talk about it with each other, and quite likely with other boys as well. They sometimes arrange, in fact, to let the information "leak" to friends not in on the experience rather than tell them directly. This heightens the exciting and daring aspects of what occurred.

Curiosity is, of course, another important reason for some boys' seeking sexual relations with prostitutes. They are curious about intercourse itself, and about what prostitutes are like. Others, particularly those who are inexperienced, are eager to find out if they can perform proficiently in a sexual relationship. As one boy said: "It was a relief to know what was involved in a sexual relationship and that I could do it." This suggests that some boys feel it quite important to secure actual sexual experience. It makes them feel more grown-up, and in their own eyes proves that they have reached manhood and can perform as males are expected to perform.

These, then, are the major reasons for teen-age boys to go to prostitutes. These same reasons make it difficult, if not impossible, for them to acknowledge to each other that the experience has been a disappointing or even possibly a very disturbing one. Quite a number run into unexpected circumstances and find the experience more than they had bargained for. When an inexperienced teen-age boy visits a prostitute, he almost certainly enters a situation in which she, rather than he, is in charge. The prostitute is older, more experienced, and on home ground. She may ask the boy if he is a "beginner," or whether he wants his sex "old-fashioned." Often such questions embarrass an inexperienced boy, and put him on the spot.

One boy said: "Up to the time she asked me that I had been trying to act very worldly-wise, and as though I had been around. Not to know what she meant made me feel very little-boy-like." A number were upset by the business-like and routine methods of the prostitutes. The most upsetting of all experiences seemed to occur when certain boys found themselves paired with a prostitute "old enough to be my mother." This expression was common when a boy had a partner who was obviously older than himself.

Most of the boys seemed to regard prostitutes as persons apart from the normal run of people. They were very commonly curious about "how they got into the business" and "why they ever entered prostitution." They may regard them as persons without feeling. One boy commented "Of course, no matter what you did to those girls you couldn't hurt them."

Some boys found the experience quite satisfactory from the sexual point of view. When their partner was an active participant in the relationship and was young, and particularly when the boys received definite physical satisfaction, they usually accounted the experience a success. Others, however, spoke of being upset by the surroundings, which they described as "dirty," "unattractive," "a barren room" or "sordid." One boy commented: "It was a place I wouldn't be caught dead in."

Upsetting, disturbing experiences such as these seemingly interfered with the sexual functioning of many of the boys. There were numerous references to an inability to attain an erection, or to reach an orgasm. Others were able to reach a climax, but found the experience quite unsatisfying. As a result some boys left the prostitute even more concerned about their sexual functioning than when they went.

POINTS THAT SHOULD BE CONSIDERED BY THOSE WHO COUNSEL TEEN-AGERS

These facts raise some interesting points for consideration by counselors who are in the position of giving guidance to teen-agers:

(1) Prostitution is obviously not out of the picture as a sexual outlet for teen-age boys. For this group it apparently served several functions—satisfaction of curiosity, enhanced feelings of masculine attainment, and as a male group experience. It is possible that—if these needs could be met some other way—the use of prostitution by such boys would diminish.

(2) The need for meaningful sex education is again pointed up. The comments and experiences of these boys indicate that learning about reproduction and anatomy is not enough—full details concerning the nature of sex and the sexual relationship are needed. Parents and educators are commonly afraid that such an elaborate presentation of facts will move boys toward experimentation and promiscuity. The subjects in this study indicate that it is the lack of facts and curiosity about them, rather than awareness of them, which causes experimentation.

(3) If almost one out of every five of these relatively unsophisticated boys has had intercourse with prostitutes, the problem of

prostitution can hardly be regarded as minor, and perhaps more emphasis should be given to it in our education of teen-agers.

(4) Society must realize that a major reason why boys visit prostitutes is that they do not feel grown-up and important to adults and to the community. More and more teen-age boys have been crowded to one side. They find it hard to get jobs where they can earn money. Their associations with adults of either sex are few. They are required to remain in school after they are physically fully grown. To some boys much of the school program appears to be useless and a waste of time.

In such circumstances boys turn to various experiences from which they hope to gain a sense of being grown-up and a feeling of masculine achievement. Sex among adults seems to be an exciting and intriguing activity. Through sexual participation the boys are able to think of themselves as adult. It is for this reason that they often use sex in an attempt to prove their masculinity and maturity, as so many boys are doing when they visit prostitutes.

If society can develop socially acceptable ways to give these boys a sense of masculine achievement, the need for them to "prove" themselves by use of sex might be diminished. This can perhaps be done by giving adolescents an opportunity to gain prestige and status in leadership positions which challenge their capacities, by giving them satisfying relationships with adults, and by including them in the significant and meaningful activities of the adult world.

Part VIII

Problems of Unwed Pregnancy and Parenthood

28

When Your Unwed Daughter Is Pregnant

by WALTER R. STOKES, LL.B., M.D.

A great many parents find themselves shocked and dismayed by news that their unmarried daughter is pregnant. During consultations with a large number of pregnant unmarried girls I have been impressed how, in families where the mother has been repressive and puritanical about sex, the girl is willing to turn anywhere rather than to her mother for counsel. Often I have heard girls declare: "I'll jump off the bridge before I'll let mother know about this!" What a commentary upon the mother's role as a sex educator!

Where the mother has been more accepting of sex, the daughter is likely to trust her and may come with her mother to the doctor's office, already having turned to her for advice. At times mother and daughter come together, with a bond of sympathy between them, but fearing the reactions of a harshly puritanical father.

As to what actually may be done when a girl is in this situation, there are a number of alternatives and the choice should be made according to circumstances in the particular case. In all cases, however, the first thing to do is to determine by physical examination and laboratory tests whether pregnancy actually exists. It is astonishing how frequently menstruation is suppressed by anxiety and fear, thus creating a false assumption of pregnancy. Accurate medical diagnosis of pregnancy is of especially grave importance when an illegal abortion is contemplated since many abortionists will carry out their procedure when there actually is no pregnancy.

Among strongly conventional families the traditional solution to an unmarried daughter's plight is insistence upon an immediate "shotgun" wedding. This means that the girl's family confronts the boy and his family with the facts and demands marriage at once, regardless of how the young people may look at it. Where the young couple are in love and would want to marry anyway, it is usually best for them to do so. But if they are not mutually in love and either one seriously resists marriage, it is far wiser not to marry. There are impressive statistics which show that a marriage entered into under protest (a true "shotgun" marriage) is likely to be wretchedly unhappy and to end in divorce.

A generation ago most clergymen insisted upon marriage of the pregnant unwed girl. In recent years, however, there has been a striking change. Now a large and increasing number of clergymen oppose marriage unless the young people are truly committed to each other and genuinely want the marriage. They take this view both because of the poor record of forced marriages and because in recent years there have been created good facilities for enabling an unwed mother to have her baby in privacy at a special institution which, in cooperation with licensed, reliable adoption agencies, can ensure a good home for the child.

Except for the unwed mother of certain minority groups, the adoption agencies have waiting lists of well-qualified childless couples who are eager to adopt. Generally they do an excellent job with their adopted children and the welfare of a child is likely to be far better served by adoption than through a forced marriage of the natural parents or by an effort of the natural mother to raise her child under the powerful stigma which our society still attaches to the children of unwed mothers.

It is clear in my mind that, if a decision is reached for an unwed girl to complete her pregnancy and place her child for adoption, she should not see the baby or know the identity of the adopting parents. If she is permitted the early care of the baby, she may be reluctant to give it up for adoption. That means, then, that the child will be raised under a painful stigma. I have often seen this happen and have the strongest reason to oppose it, at least until such time as our society can overcome its brutal hostility toward the child of an unwed mother.

Much has been written and said about the alleged guilty, morbid feelings of a girl who gives up her baby for adoption. I believe this has been vastly exaggerated. Unless those about her behave in a way to create guilt, I have rarely found it a serious or persistent problem.

THE ABORTION SITUATION TODAY

Many pregnant unwed girls think desperately and solely in terms of obtaining an abortion, legally if possible, illegally if necessary. Such thinking sometimes occurs even when there is a mutual desire of the young people for marriage. They simply may not want to marry under the stigma of a premarital pregnancy. Here I feel that they should accept the pregnancy and plan to marry soon because under these conditions there is usually no legal way to obtain an abortion and the available persons who will perform one illegally are likely to be dangerously unskilled.

Under existing law the reasons that justify a legal abortion are very few and will not apply at all in the vast majority of cases. The reason most often used is that, for psychiatric reasons, the sanity and perhaps the life of the girl is gravely threatened if her pregnancy is allowed to continue. Abortion for this reason is done with some frequency, in a few of our states, among our well-to-do people, but is rarely applied to poor girls or to girls from minority groups. I deplore this kind of discrimination but am obliged to report it as a fact of current medical practice.

Many pregnant unwed girls, and quite often their desperate parents, are insistent upon trying to find an illegal abortionist if the pregnancy can not be interrupted by legal means. Some have a mistaken idea that there are plenty of skillful, reliable abortionists about if one only knows how to reach them. This expectation is in fact poorly justified. Some years ago there were a few physicians scattered about the country who devoted all their time to performing abortions illegally but in a medically skilled way. Today their number is exceedingly small, while medically unqualified abortionists have become more numerous. The latter operate in great secrecy, charge exorbitant fees and often either fail to induce abortion or else they bring about hazardous infection and other dangerous complications. Any girl or her parents should be wary of falling into the hands of such unskilled persons.

Most of our present laws governing the legally justified use of abortion are regarded by many physicians as inhumanly harsh and restrictive. Recently there has been considerable talk among liberal physicians and lawyers about rewriting our abortion laws to accord with enlightened modern views. The American Law Institute has prepared a model law intended as a guide for the revision of our out-of-date state laws and Colorado and North Carolina have become the first states to enact legislation which closely follows the proposed model. The American Medical Association has now voted to support certain changes in abortion laws, and legislatures of many states are considering proposals to change their laws.

It must be noted that the new Colorado law (and others like it now under consideration) does not sanction abortion merely because a pregnancy is inconvenient or unwanted. Abortion is approved only where continuation of the pregnancy would gravely jeopardize the life or health of the prospective mother; where there is medical evidence that the child is likely to be born with a severe abnormality; where the pregnancy has resulted from rape; or where the girl involved is of tender years (usually fifteen or less). The new Colorado law is a step in the right direction but it does not permit consideration of factors involving economic stress or social welfare, as do the recent laws of some foreign countries.

While abortion will always be a distasteful procedure to any sensitive physician, it clearly has a place to meet certain hazards involving both mother and child. Some of our more liberal physicians feel that social and economic reasons should be gravely considered. Under our existings laws these reasons have no validity.

It is obvious that this legal situation generates the pressure that drives more than a million American women to illegal abortionists each year, with all the personal agony and illness or death that may follow. Some physicians firmly believe that this tragic aspect of our culture could be virtually eliminated if we were to revise our ancient, punitive thinking concerning unwed pregnant girls. They believe we should liberalize our legally acceptable reasons for abortion and redefine criminal abortion as essentially that which is performed by an unlicensed, untrained person. To achieve this will be truly a landmark advance in public health and the practice of sound preventive medicine.

A notable amount of progress in this direction has already been made in some other lands, particularly Denmark, Sweden, Rumania, Japan, and Great Britain. In the Scandinavian countries not only have reasons for abortion been humanely liberalized but, of equal importance, the traditional stigma attaching to birth out of wedlock has been largely overcome. Some desperate American women have gone to foreign lands to seek abortion, often being turned down on arrival. A few have been successful in Japan but obviously the expense and other difficulties are formidable.

In our country it may be foreseen that, as sex continues to be appreciated in a more rational, enlightened way and as contraceptives become more simple and effective, mothers will accept responsibility to see that their daughters are so well informed that pregnancy in the unwed girl will become a rarity instead of the all-too-common tragedy it is today.

There are a number of reputable agencies throughout the United States that provide maternity and adoption services for the unwed mother. Any girl who desires to make use of these services should apply early in her pregnancy in order that she and her child may receive the best of prenatal care.

29

Spotlight On the Unwed Father

by CLARK E. VINCENT, PH.D.

The biological fathers of illegitimate children are both condemned and coddled, by the public in general and unwed mothers in particular. The public makes scapegoats of them with such labels as "sexual exploiters" and "defilers of youth"—*but it exerts little effort either to identify them or to impose financial responsibilities on them.*

Unwed mothers may bitterly accuse the fathers of "deception," "betrayal" and "desertion"—*but they usually assure them a protective anonymity by being unwilling to identify them.* In some cases, of course, the fathers are but pawns of unwed mothers, who use them only to resolve their own psychological problems and deprive the fathers of the dignity of even having an identity.

There is only *one* study of unmarried fathers for about every *thirty* studies of unwed mothers. This is an indication of a basic dilemma confronting those who seek to understand and decrease illegitimacy. We have two choices: either we must be willing to critically examine, and possibly change, some attitudes and practices we prefer neither to examine nor to change—or we must settle for having a very limited understanding of illegitimacy.

In the case of unmarried fathers, we must either change the traditional double standard by which we are more lenient toward sexual misbehavior in males than in females—or we must remain satisfied with the conventional efforts which presume to understand illegitimacy by studying only *half* its cause, the unwed mothers.

That we generally subscribe to, and resist changes in, this double standard is evidenced by the following: (a) we condemn and stigmatize unmarried mothers far more harshly than we do unmarried fathers; (b) we tend to express greater indignation about wives than about husbands involved in extramarital affairs; (c) wives are more frequently blamed than husbands for unwanted pregnancies occurring within marriage; (d) state legislators propose tubal ligations to sterilize unmarried women who become pregnant repeatedly, but remain silent about vasectomies to sterilize men who make unmarried women repeatedly pregnant.

Although this double standard of preferential treatment to males has a long history and broader application in such areas as unequal pay and promotion opportunities for men and women, it is reversed in some cases of so-called sexual perversion. An oversimplified example of this is the following: When a male watches a female undress, he is labeled a "peeping Tom," but when a female watches a male undress, the male is called an "exhibitionist."

The double standard is not the only reason, however, why we regard the female rather than the male as the subject for study and the object of censure in illegitimacy. *The female poses problems, the male does not.* It is she for whom prenatal care, maternity homes, and possible child support must be financed; and it is her changing profile which openly threatens traditional sex mores. The male represents no obvious expense to taxpayers and shows no evidence of unconventional sex behavior. Moreover, the woman's need for care during pregnancy and delivery makes her available for study and identifiable for censure. The man's biological role ends at conception, and society's protection of him by lack of interest enables him to remain anonymous and unavailable for study.

Recognizing that such social attitudes and practices have made an enigma of the unmarried father, my purpose in this article is to share some *impressions* and *hunches* based primarily on individual interview and counseling sessions with thirty-seven such fathers. In twenty-one cases, the females they impregnated were also seen. A secondary source of these impressions is the data on more than one thousand unmarried fathers, as reported in questionnaire form by unmarried mothers.

These are some of my major impressions:

(1) *Unmarried fathers represent a cross section of American males.* The socioeconomic backgrounds of unmarried fathers appear to be fairly similar to those of American males in general *when the information derived from various groups of unwed mothers is combined.* The unwed mothers attended in a county hospital, who were predominantly Negroes of low economic level, reported being impregnated by Negro males of a similar low economic level.

The maternity-home mothers who were predominantly young white high-school students were impregnated by young white high-school and college males. The mothers attended by physicians in private practice were predominantly white and in their twenties and thirties, were employed in white-collar and professional jobs, and over 40 per cent had attended college. They were impregnated predominantly by white college-educated middle-class males employed in a wide range of white-collar and professional jobs.

Among these men, for example, were 42 salesmen, 15 business owners or office managers, 11 teachers, 7 lawyers, 5 physicians, 5 executives, 4 professors, 3 dentists, 2 ministers, 2 reporters, 2 engineers, a pilot, a musician, a chiropractor, an accountant, and a bank clerk.

(2) *Derogatory descriptions of unmarried fathers are labels after the act.* Of 1,062 unwed mothers studied, only 3 per cent reported that their sex union involved "force, rape or incest." Thirty-two per cent reported "a love relationship of some duration"; 23 per cent indicated "a close friendship relationship"; 25 per cent said it was "a casual relationship"; and 17 per cent didn't classify their relationship.

On the basis of such reports, it is my impression that such terms as "sexual exploiter" represent *ex post facto* labels that are affixed to the male *after* pregnancy occurs *and* the female remains unmarried. Such labeling becomes a way of berating the male, not for having illicit coition, *but for not protecting the female via marriage.*

Support for using this or similar labels usually involves a highly selective interpretation of data showing the age and socioeconomic superiority of males over the females they illicitly impregnate. However, this superiority appears to be quite similar to that generally of husbands over wives. It is consistent with usual courting and marrying patterns which traditionally favor that males be slightly taller, a little older, and better educated than the females they court and wed.

The tendency to accept various derogatory labels for unmarried fathers at face value is misleading—it too easily deters us from considering the probability that the majority of illicit pregnancies occur within the context of friendship or love relationships which at the time are perceived as positive and good. It also keeps us from openly recognizing the contradiction inherent in our greater censure of illicit pregnancy (which is the *result*) than of illicit intercourse (which is the *cause*).

(3) *Unmarried fathers experience fairly intense conflicting feelings toward the females they impregnate and the children they beget.*

The readiness with which they take advantage of the protective anonymity and irresponsibility proffered by society and by unwed mothers may too easily deceive us into believing that unmarried fathers go merrily on their way without remorse or guilt. And although many such fathers are quick to assert either that they had no feelings of guilt and responsibility, or that they quickly resolved such feelings, they just as quickly supply explanations which suggest the contrary.

If married, the male may emphasize that the female involved preferred no help or further contact for fear of becoming known as the "other woman." Or he may express his suspicions that his wife has previously been similarly involved. If single, he may readily cite the advice of the family physician and/or that of the girl's parents to the effect that it is to the advantage of all concerned to sever all ties, including any financial help that might imply future marital obligations.

Valid and quasi-soothing as such types of reasons may be, they inwardly distress the male reared in a society where the masculine role is to protect, and not to be protected by, the female. The fathers who do maintain contact with their illicit sex partners are further demasculinized when unable even to see, much less take pride in, their offspring. And although it might commonly be thought they have no interest in doing so, the comments, questions, and implicit wishes expressed to me by unmarried fathers lead me to believe a sizable proportion of them do.

Whether it be called the male ego, the deep-seated desire to create and produce, or the showing of virility, there is something in a man of any walk of life which exacts a price when he is denied identification with that which he has helped create, even when the denial is of his own choosing.

(4) *Unmarried fathers partially resolve their conflicting feelings by way of derogatory stereotyping of unwed mothers.* There is another category of rationale which the unmarried father employs in convincing himself and others that he has not guilt or obligations. This consists of his derogatory evaluations of his sex partner. His mildest portrayal will include such statements as the following taken from case histories: "She was old enough to know what she was doing." "She encouraged it as much as I did." "She went into it with her eyes open." "She could have said no."

(The frequency and persistence of this theme, if better documented and heard by the public, might counterbalance the current selective emphasis upon "very young" unwed mothers.)

A far more disparaging picture is painted by other unmarried fathers, some of whom one suspects are struggling less successfully with their feelings of guilt and/or inadequacy; and it is these descriptions that over the years have undoubtedly contributed to, and prolonged, the misleading and negative stereotyping of unwed mothers: "Why should I think it's mine when I know half a dozen guys who've had her." "She asked for it, always teasing everybody in the office. She's nothing but a slut. If it hadn't been me, it would be someone else sooner or later." "Why shouldn't she take the consequences? She got paid for it twice over in all the parties, trips, and good times and even clothes I bought her. She has a hell of a lot more now than when I met her." "Why should I worry about her, she's either sly like a fox or too stupid to be with men. I'm glad to be rid of her. She forgot too easily to be a good receptionist, but I think she was bright enough to use pregnancy to try to hook me."

(5) *The unmarried father's lack of a tangible involvement in the processes of pregnancy and birth tends to prolong whatever guilt feelings he may have.* The male does not have to endure the physical discomforts of nine months of pregnancy and the labor

pains of birth. Nor does he have to face the censorious comments and stares of others and wrestle with the decision about whether to keep or to release the baby for adoption.

In fact, the enormity of what the unmarried mother must face is such as to usually make us forget that the physical discomfort of pregnancy and the pain of birth may afford her a form of "punishment," a degree of atonement, unavailable to the unmarried father. Also, for some unmarried mothers there is a feeling of retribution derived from having supported the traditional concepts of motherhood; for example, courageously completing pregnancy even though afraid, away from loved ones, and censured. And difficult as the decision may be, many unwed mothers experience a sense of at least partial retribution to society when their illicit pregnancies subsequently make it possible for childless couples to achieve the cherished goal of having a family.

My intent in the foregoing discussion is not to minimize the lopsidedness with which the burdens of stigma, hardships, and responsibilities in illegitimacy are borne by females. Rather, it is to illustrate the extent of our ignorance about the unmarried father. Such ignorance distorts our understanding of unmarried mothers and impedes the diminution of illegitimacy.

Part I X

*Coping with Anxieties
About Homosexuality*

30

Parents and Homosexuality

by WARDELL B. POMEROY, PH.D.

The very word "homosexuality" is apt to stir feelings of abhorrence in many of us. It brings to mind something sinister, furtive, forbidden. In America, homosexual behavior is a crime and our jails hold many men convicted of this charge. But sometimes if you examine a subject that has horrified you, objectively and dispassionately, you find the abhorrence you originally felt will be reduced and perhaps even vanish. This chapter is an effort to present objectively and dispassionately some facts and ideas concerning homosexuality which, I hope, may serve to dispel some of the upsetting or disquieting feelings parents may have about this "distasteful" subject.

One thing that surprises many people is to learn that our culture is not in the mainstream of current thinking about homosexuality. For example, of 193 different cultures studied by Murdock, only 14 per cent rejected male homosexuality, whereas 28 per cent accepted it. In 58 per cent of these cultures, male homosexuality was accepted under some circumstances and rejected under others. Of 225 American Indian tribes studied by Murdock, 53 per cent accepted male homosexuality, with only 24 per cent completely rejecting it.

A number of ancient cultures accepted homosexuality. For example, the Greeks looked on homosexual behavior as permissible and even desirable under certain circumstances. Many cultures currently hold this attitude, including groups in the Near East and Africa.

Our own sexual codes, growing out of Judeo-Christian codes, have been more restrictive as far as sex is concerned than almost any other system of morals. These codes were based on the belief that all sexual behavior that did not lead to procreation was to be condemned. Thus procreation and sexual behavior have become irretrievably interlinked in our culture, rather than procreation being considered a byproduct of a small fraction of 1 per cent of sexual behavior.

WHAT DO WE MEAN BY HOMOSEXUALITY?

We might well start off by asking, "What do we mean by homosexuality?" One can mean either a physical contact between two members of the same sex which brings a sexual response (which may lead to an orgasm) or one may mean a psychological response to a member of one's own sex. This response can occur through thought, sight, remembering past experiences, or anticipating future ones. Usually the physical and the psychological go hand-in-hand although there are some occasions when they occur separately.

One of the basic errors made in a discussion of homosexuality is the idea that it is a discrete entity, that it is something entirely separate from heterosexuality. Even doctors have a tendency to fall into this error. They speak of someone as "a homosexual" rather than a person taking part in homosexual behavior.

We might also ask how much homosexual behavior someone has to experience before he is "a homosexual." For instance, I know a man who reported having had homosexual contact with more than 10,000 different males (he actually kept records) but he was still more heterosexual than homosexual. The *number* of women with whom he had been sexually intimate amounted to a mere 600 or 700, but the *frequency* with which he engaged in heterosexual contact was much greater, and his psychological responses were much stronger to females than to males. *Could this man be called "a homosexual?"*

While only about a third of human males and a sixth of human females engage in overt homosexual activity, about half of the males either have had overt homosexual relations or have been sexually aroused by males. For males, then, homosexuality is *statistically* almost normal, whereas for females it is not.

There are a fair number of married males who have homosexual relations while married—about 10 per cent, according to the Kinsey Report. Some of these males are more homosexual than heterosexual even though they continue to have intercourse with their wives.

The Institute for Sex Research has devised a seven-point scale which categorizes males and females as to their homosexual-heterosexual balance. A "zero" is a person who is exclusively heterosexual whereas a "six" is one who is exclusively homosexual. According to this scale, a "three" would be someone who experienced about as much of heterosexuality as homosexuality and had no preference for one over the other. The married males who prefer homosexual to heterosexual relations, referred to above, would be "fours" in this scale. In the majority of cases, they find it difficult to continue their marriage for a long period of time.

Many people are confused by the concept of "latent homosexuality." This embodies the idea that a person may have had homosexual desires which have been repressed, or, in other words, have not been allowed to come into his consciousness. However, these desires do not disappear (according to this theory) but continue to exist in the unconscious part of his mind and cause conflict with his conscious heterosexual desires.

The concept of latent homosexuality has also been used as synonymous with psychological response. If someone is aroused psychologically by a member of his own sex but does not have actual physical contact with the person who stimulates him, he is a "latent homosexual." Since all of us have the potentiality to commit every conceivable criminal and antisocial act (we are all "latent" murderers, arsonists, rapists, etc.), the concept of latent homosexuality is not a very meaningful one.

Many person who have never taken part in a homosexual act, nonetheless may be stirred by a sexual feeling toward someone of the same sex through fantasying, dreaming or being psychologically stimulated in other ways. They become horror-stricken and feel very guilty about this "perverted" feeling. Some male patients in my practice in marriage counseling have on occasion reported dreams of sexual contact with other men (even their fathers), or they have had fleeting thoughts of other males while masturbating. This is sometimes more upsetting to them than actual overt homosexual behavior would be. They feel themselves some sort of monster. If they lived in another culture, one that was more accepting of homosexuality, they would not need to go through the anguish our culture imposes on them.

HOW CAN PARENTS HELP

Parents may often be unduly upset believing that their sons are experiencing some of the same anguish as a result of their homosexual fantasies. They should remember it is during adolescence that a boy becomes aware most intensely of the taboos against homosexuality. In taking sexual histories of young boys for the Kinsey Report, I found that it was easier to elicit from them their pre-pubescent (puberty occurs at age twelve or thirteen) homosexual play than their heterosexual play, as the homosexual activity was not considered to be as taboo in the earlier years. But adults, in trying to remember their pre-pubescent sex play, had a much easier time in describing their heterosexual activity before puberty than their homosexual activity because the taboos taking effect just after puberty had been well ingrained over the years.

How can a parent help a son if he seems to be suffering tormenting thoughts about his homosexual fantasies? If you wait for him to broach the subject himself, you will wait forever. Children quickly learn that such topics as homosexuality are not welcomed for discussion by most parents. The parent must take the initiative by bringing up the subject himself; for instance, he can use current events to educate his child in the sexual area just as he does in other areas of life.

A newspaper article about a man arrested on a homosexual charge or a child molestation charge might prove to be the vehicle to introduce this subject to a child, for example. Books, plays, movies, and even television may sometimes serve as the entering wedge. Just as this chapter, and this book, are bringing a subject considered "taboo" out into the open for discussion, so a parent's discussion with his child may accomplish the same purpose. A discussion that is quiet, objective, thoughtful, and factual will accomplish much more than one that conveys to the child what may be a parent's feelings of hostility, bewilderment, and resentment toward homosexuality.

We might ask here: "How can someone be identified as homosexual?" It is estimated that about 15 per cent of the males with extensive homosexual histories, and 5 per cent of the females, are identifiable as homosexual. This identification is made in the male by noting such signs as limp wrists, swishy walks, and other affected mannerisms, sometimes the wearing of extreme clothing which almost caricatures the opposite sex, and particularly by the emotional interaction that a person may show to another individual who is of the same sex.

However these signs are by no means infallible, as there are many males with the above "stigmata" who are not homosexual in the least. Conversely, it must be remembered that the cowboys and the Indian fighters of the West (the stereotype of the American he-man) probably indulged in more homosexual behavior than any other group of men in the country. Even males who dress as females (transvestites) are not necessarily homosexual in the slightest.

If parents fear that a son (or daughter) is exhibiting signs of homosexuality, they are undoubtedly concerned as to what steps they can take to eradicate the signs. If you will forgive an oversimplified analogy, one cannot learn to like ice cream by giving up cake. Nor can one learn to develop heterosexually by giving up homosexuality. Hence, I would urge a positive approach rather than a negative one. Every opportunity that you, as a parent, can take to help your son develop heterosexually, to have a social (and this does not rule out the possibility of a sexual) contact with a girl, will lead him away from homosexuality.

Our culture actually promotes homosexuality for the younger teen-age boy and discourages heterosexuality. The average American parent is all too inclined to tease a son about his early fumbling attempts at dating girls. To a sensitive boy, this may put the damper on his budding heterosexuality.

This applies to daughters, too, in their need to give up feelings of Lesbianism and turn to males outside the family. One of my women patients recalled of her grammar- and high-school days that every time she brought home a boy, her father would make a disparaging remark such as, "He hasn't the table manners of a gorilla," or "Doesn't he have the price of a haircut?" Such discouragement of heterosexuality will only put distance between children and their parents and will not accomplish the desired effect. On the other hand, by encouraging a child's heterosexuality, a parent may very well decrease the distance between the child and himself and lead the child in the desired direction of heterosexuality.

WHY DO SOME PEOPLE HAVE HOMOSEXUAL RELATIONS?

Why do people have homosexual relations? The more appropriate question is: Why doesn't *everybody* have homosexual relations? As mentioned earlier, there exist cultures where nearly everyone does have homosexual relations. We know, too, that in all other species of mammals (and man *is* a mammal), homosexual activity is found everywhere. The fact that this does not hold true for our culture is an indication of the inhibiting effect the culture has had on us.

Yet, in spite of the strong, existing taboos in our culture, why do so many people still become homosexual? In our present stage of knowledge, we can only say that there are probably many different ways in which the sexual pattern can develop. There are several common beliefs that are probably untrue. Some maintain a person is born homosexual. It is extremely doubtful, in my opinion, that homosexuality is inborn, despite some research that has pointed in this direction. If any genetic factors do play a part, they do so undoubtedly in an indirect way. It is also very doubtful that constitutional, or hormonal factors are related to homosexuality, except also in a very indirect way. For example, a child might have a hormonal imbalance that would cause him to be extremely obese. This obesity might make it difficult for him to develop a heterosexual pattern and hence he might develop homosexuality by default.

It is also not clear as to whether early seduction is a cause of homosexuality. Seduction may be a triggering mechanism for homosexual development, but the child must somehow be ready in order for the seduction to take hold. There are too many boys who have been seduced by older males who have *not* developed homosexually to make the act of seduction a very important cause.

I believe that one of the ways in which it is possible for a homosexual pattern to develop is through the failure to develop heterosexually. Because there are only two sexes, if one wishes to have a sexual relationship with another person and does not develop this with the opposite sex, he has but one sex left, namely, his own. Thus, males who are fearful of girls, or who learn to despise them (hate and fear are probably very closely interrelated), will sometimes develop a homosexual life by default.

The same principle sometimes holds true for males with physical defects, acne, obesity, extreme variations in height, and other anomalies. Under these circumstances, they find it less difficult to adjust socially (and also sexually) to members of their own sex than to members of the opposite sex. Boys with defects of this type, or with extreme fear or hatred of the opposite sex, need a very special urging, perhaps even prodding by their parents, to be helped along the road to heterosexuality. The parents must exercise a very special ingenuity to aid such sons.

Another way, I believe, that homosexuality can develop may seem paradoxical to the above. From ages eight to thirteen (these ages are rough approximations), males ally themselves with other males. This male alliance develops into gangs, and into friendships where mutual security is achieved. The male who fails to be taken into the male alliance will often emulate males who are in the alliance and this emulation will sometimes develop into a sexual interest.

Thus parents, it seems to me, have a dual role. They should encourage their sons to feel at ease with, and become interested in, females, and they should also encourage them to become "one of the gang" as far as males are concerned. For faulty relations either with one's own sex or the opposite sex is probably one of the greatest reasons for the development of homosexuality in males or females.

Little has been said here about the "Oedipus complex," although some have believed that this is one of the major causes of homosexuality. According to this theory, the boy, because of a deep erotic desire for his mother, develops an extreme fear of the incest taboo and then generalizes his mother to mean all women. Hence, he is unable to have sexual relations with any woman, since they all symbolize his mother and death would be the penalty for his daring incest. It is possible that such fantasies can exist in a boy's mind and lead to homosexual activity as the lesser of two evils. But it is highly problematic that this occurs in very many cases.

THE AUTHOR'S ADVICE TO PARENTS

A last word to parents: the father who is afraid of his own homosexual interest, or who is very fearful of his son developing a homosexual interest, will tend to push his son away from him. He will look on his own bodily contact with his son, such as hugging or kissing, as effeminate and undesirable. Such a father may be so upset himself over his homosexual feelings that he is very likely to implant the same fears and concerns in his son.

The detached, remote mother who pushes her son away physically because of a fear of her sexual feelings toward him, is even more likely to create the very confusion in him that she is trying to avoid. Without an early responsiveness to the mother, the possibility of a son's sexual adjustment to some other female in later life is reduced. As in every other area of life, moderate expression of feeling by both parents is in order. For, if a parent goes to the opposite extreme, and cannot restrain himself from always touching or hugging or kissing the child hungrily, what he may believe to be warmth and affection turns into a sexual seduction that serves only to further confuse and bewilder the child.

Because so much emotion is engendered by homosexual behavior, even doctors often respond as lay people, rather than as doctors, in their treatment of homosexuals. For this reason, it is not enough to go to a psychiatrist, a psychologist, or other therapist with a problem of homosexuality, *but it is necessary to go to one who is particularly astute and understanding about this area.* It has been my experience, unfortunately, that such experts in human behavior are very much in the minority.

We are just starting to understand the very complex problem of homosexuality and anyone who says he has "the" answer, may be looked at with distrust. Hopefully, most parents will be able, out of their understanding and compassion, to give their sons and daughters the warmth, love, and support that will ensure their adjustment in life as healthy, effective, and happy. It is even possible that homosexual behavior may not be so abhorrent and sinister as many persons would have it, so that when a son or daughter engages in homosexual activity, there is still a reasonable chance that a healthy, effective, and happy life can ensue.

31

Adolescent Homosexual Fears

by LESTER A. KIRKENDALL, PH.D.

For a boy to admit that he is worried about homosexual experiences or feelings is difficult. Most fellows would rather admit almost anything else relating to sex than this. Their reluctance to acknowledge homosexual feelings or experiences is quite understandable. They are simply expressing the same fear of, and dislike for, homosexuality that is found throughout our society.

In surveys that I have conducted on sexual worries and concerns of boys, about one out of every five boys said he was, or had been, concerned in some respect about homosexuality. In a group of fifty college-age boys who were questioned, the proportion was slightly higher. When boys who expressed *possible* concern about homosexuality were added, the proportion was increased to about one in four. Most of the boys with whom I have talked were between the ages of sixteen and twenty-two. Those who were worried about actual "homosexual" experiences, in almost all instances, mentioned experiences with other adolescents.

These associations were usually experiments resulting in part from curiosity and a need for more information about sex in one's self and others. Unable to get help from reliable sources, the boys sought understanding from each other. Their efforts would have shocked their parents, and they left the boys with feelings of guilt, but at that stage of development and under the circumstances, what they had done is done by many.

Alfred was an eighteen-year-old boy who was ashamed and worried over earlier homosexual experimentation. At about fourteen to fifteen years of age, Alfred and two of his boyfriends had on several occasions engaged in genital examination, and masturbatory exchanges. Usually these experiences involved only two of the boys, though on one or two occasions all three had participated.

"I think I know why I did it," Alfred explained to me, "though I'm not sure this would apply to the other boys. I was the only boy in the family. My parents were both prudish, and sex or physical development was never mentioned in any way in the family. I never saw either male or female undressed. Even at school I didn't take part in sports or gym activities that resulted in boys undressing before each other, though I did exchange such sexual information as I had with other boys.

"My own sexual maturation occurred when I was about fourteen. I was not well prepared for it, and it both excited and bothered me. My two boyfriends were having similar experiences and were as poorly informed as I was. I think we were just so curious we had to find out in some way and we did it by experimenting with each other. That way we actually came to know something about genital size, what happened when an orgasm occurred, and what seminal discharges were. I know it was not what we should have done. I can't feel right about it yet, but I can't help wondering if it isn't just as normal as examining each other's muscles."

Some boys—even though they have never engaged in sex play with other boys—are bothered by occasional feelings that they would like to. They are disturbed because they think a satisfactory adjustment requires that one feel sexual attraction for, and respond sexually to, members of the other sex only. They do not know there is a period in normal development, near the time of puberty and in early adolescence, when both boys and girls feel a strong emotional and physical attraction for members of the same sex.

This attraction is usually displayed through close and exclusive friendships and displays of affection. These feelings, however, are easily transferred into physical response. In general, two persons with affection for each other want to touch and embrace one another—to have close bodily contact. Little wonder then that two adolescent boys, close pals, have physical contacts which lead to genital explorations and sexual associations. Such experiences satisfy both their desire to be close and their curiosity, and also give them physical pleasure.

BOYS' WORRIES ARE RELIEVED
WHEN THEY GAIN AN UNDERSTANDING OF
PHYSICAL AND SEXUAL MATURATION

If theories about developmental stages, the nature of homosexuality, and the meaning of human behavior seem much emphasized in this article, there are reasons. First, much trouble and many needless worries arise from general ignorance and dangerous misconceptions about the meaning of homosexual feelings and conduct. The fears which result ordinarily do more harm than the experiences themselves ever could. Second, most boys seem to find real relief from their worries when they have gained a clearer concept of the normal processes of physical and sexual growing up. When they realize that every one goes through a period of being keenly interested in members of the same sex, they then see that they are not abnormal. Their sense of guilt is relieved, and they are much more able to cope with their problems.

This approach is helpful in relieving the worries of boys when their sexual associations have been with persons quite a bit older than they are. A boy who has been having an experience with a confirmed homosexual, will need a general explanation of the causes of homosexuality.

Dave and Tom, two boys who had had experiences with older persons, were helped by such explanations. Dave, age nineteen, was concerned because on a hitchhiking trip he had been approached twice by older men. As a high-school boy he had also been accosted once. This all added up to his conclusion: "I must look like a homosexual. What do they see in me? Or do I act like one?" Dave may have experienced more advances from older men than is common, but his fear stemmed from the mistaken belief that "you can tell a homosexual when you see one—by the way he talks, walks, and moves." Since Dave believed this, he was a ready prey for fears and worries after he had been approached.

Tom was twenty-one years of age. He had agreed to act as handler for a group of athletes. One evening a boy with a leg cramp asked Tom to rub out the kink. As Tom rubbed he found himself with an erection. "I finished that rubdown," he said, "but I decided I would do no more. I just wonder why I responded that way." Further conversation made clear the basis for Tom's decision. When he was about fourteen, he had been seduced by a young man about twenty-five with whom he had become well acquainted. Tom had not wanted to respond but he had. He did not want to enjoy it but he did.

Only one experience had occurred, but afterward Tom felt very guilty. He also wondered if, as a result, he might become homosexual. He had repressed his fear and guilt so thoroughly that it had not come to the surface again until the rubdown situation.

Boys, like Tom, who do not have a definite and well-established heterosexual pattern are particularly likely to react as he did. He was very much in the normal adolescent homosexual stage, but felt that he should respond as he would at a later period of development. It is possible that both Tom and Dave responded as they did because they were concealing and repressing strong homosexual desires. But even if they were, certainly their unreasoning fears did not help. Tom's awareness that such responses as he had experienced could be explained in several ways was helpful to him.

Some boys worried because they took the lead in getting into homosexual play. John is an example. John was a high school senior. About four years before, he had encouraged his cousin, a boy his own age, to engage in sex play with him. This has occurred only once, but John was fearful that his seduction might some time cause his cousin to become a homosexual. Each time he saw his cousin he was reminded of this experience and was troubled again. Shame over what had occurred made it impossible ever to mention his concern to his cousin. John was relieved to know that confirmed homosexuality is produced by deep-seated forces to which an individual is exposed over an extended period of time. No one is made a homosexual by a single, isolated experience.

The problem of fears about possible homosexuality is complicated by the rivalries and hostilities that exist between the sexes and by the lower status accorded to women. In our society men have a problem of attaining a real sense of masculine achievement and worth. This increases their fear that they may be homosexual, causing them to be disturbed many times when there is no need for it. But in spite of these circumstances, the situation would be much helped if we could not only have plain, common-sense facts about homosexuality but could learn to accept these facts. The problems of the boys with whom I have talked have been greatly intensified by unreasoning and needless fears. A rational and understanding attitude toward homosexual experiences and feelings is most helpful in preventing and relieving such fears.

Part X

Helping the Handicapped Develop Sexually

32

Sex and the Handicapped

by HELEN K. BRANSON, M.A., AND
RALPH BRANSON, M.A.

Very frequently, family, friends, and teachers become so engrossed in assisting the physically handicapped adolescent with his physical and educational problems that they neglect to think of him as an emotional individual. Most people think of his emotions only when he becomes a problem. What they fail to understand is that the physically disabled adolescent is caught in a vise. He must develop an emotional shell that will help him to fight back against his disappointments. At the same time he yearns for the same warmth, affection, and sexual fulfillment that others are encouraged to pursue.

The love of parents and friends is helpful, but it is not enough. What the handicapped person fears is that he will never have a mate. It is against this fear that he tries to insulate himself. This does not refer to young men whose handicap interferes with normal potency. We are here discussing those who fear that they may never have the *opportunity* to form a sexual relationship.

A few may react to their worries by actively seeking sexual partners. But more often, the handicapped adolescent reacts with strong hostility whenever he finds the vise of anxiety closing in around him.

One important factor is how the adolescent sees himself. This is significant not only to handicapped people, but to normal adolescents as well. By experimentation, training, and activity the normal youth gradually attains a body image that reassures him. He becomes convinced that he will be accepted as a marriage partner when the time comes. But the handicapped young person finds on every side strong evidence that his chances are slim indeed.

First of all, his parents frequently fail to encourage his independence. During his childhood he receives much attention. Efforts are made to minimize his difficulty. He knows that he is deeply indebted to his mother and father for these things. Yet at the same time, there is deeply ingrained hostility and resentment against having to feel this gratitude. The disabled adolescent thus often becomes hostile, morose, and difficult to advise.

Secondly, as the child enters adolescence he develops a strong need to be like other teen-agers. He wants to use their language, dress as they do, cut his hair as they do. But he knows full well that he has always been different. This difference suddenly becomes important and embarrassing beyond remedy.

Failure in any activity may be difficult for him to face. But sometimes he needs failure in order to realize where his limitations begin and leave off. He needs to know that he cannot have everything that he desires just because life has dealt him a cruel blow. For if he does not come to know these things, he cannot become an individual worthy of love, or even capable of loving.

One might say that sexual satisfaction is not necessarily linked to love. But in the case of the physically limited adolescent they are more closely entwined than in the normal individual. For what this adolescent fears is not being chosen, if one is a female, or being refused, if he is the male. And he thinks his physical handicap is the biggest stumbling block to his gaining this love. He fears that not being considered physically and sexually attractive also prevents others from loving him.

JOB OF THOSE WHO DEAL WITH THE HANDICAPPED

Those who deal with the handicapped must accept their developing sexuality; they must provide them with means for becoming real persons, with assets that others will seek. They must be taught how to be good hosts or hostesses, how to find the moderate means of expressing feelings, yet be tactful and considerate of others. Their parents must overcome their own image of these youngsters as helpless or partially helpless treasures in whom they have invested so much of themselves that they resent any outside attachments.

Take the case of Mary Ann. She is an able girl in mathematics. Crippled by cerebral palsy, it was many years before she mastered many self-care details such as dressing, etc. Her parents were devoted and attentive. They encouraged her to study mathematics, and she entered college. In high school, however, she was never encouraged to have social contacts. Instead she was encouraged to develop individual hobbies, such as music appreciation. Whenever friends came, they were received politely but the mother made it clear that they were not to stay too long nor come too often, as Mary Ann must study and rest.

At college Mary Ann was swept off her feet by her first date. She immediately assumed his attentions were serious, and he was so frightened by her needs for his reassurance that he avoided dating her again. The second time that Mary Ann had a date, she had made up her mind she wasn't going to lose out again. She not only responded to his mild caresses after the football game, but openly offered sexual encouragement. The young man was confused, and out of curiosity dated her again. She repeated her exaggerated reactions, and he decided that if she wished so desperately for physical attention, he would provide it.

Another case illustrating the reaction of a handicapped individual is that of Jack. At nineteen he was permanently crippled following an automobile accident. His parents have instilled in him the idea that although he is college material there is no need for him to obtain an education beyond high school, as he will inherit their property later on. For the present he must work for them, helping to run their small apartment houses. Other brothers and sisters have been completely cut out of the family will with only token inheritances.

Whenever Jack wants to assert his independence in any way, his parents block him. They discourage any girls in the neighborhood who even speak to him, and the mother talks to him long and often about the dangers of getting girls into "trouble." She warns him against masturbation, saying it will make him perverted and keep his mind on sex—which she insists is never going to be for him.

In the first place, neither of these families is accepting the feminine or masculine role of the crippled youth. Mary Ann and Jack have been considered nonsexual entities by their parents. Consequently their sexual anxieties have been increased.

Parents should endeavor to provide five essential factors in the emotional development of the physically handicapped youth:

(1) A stable home in which the child is encouraged to accentuate what he can do, rather than what he cannot do.

(2) A friendly environment where the child can discuss his limitations and come to grips with his own sexual feelings.

(3) A social environment in which the young person develops skills, talents, and outlets that will help him to compensate for his limitations.

(4) As much independence as possible, even when he makes mistakes.

(5) A goal of eventual independence from the family whenever the handicap permits.

Normal sexuality is just as important for handicapped people as for others. They want to have a home, children, and sexual expression and satisfaction. A few are forced by virtue of their handicaps to suppress their sexual desires. But the majority—many more than most people realize—can be satisfactory wives or husbands.

33

Sex Education of Mentally Retarded Children

By WARREN R. JOHNSON, ED.D.

Each semester, of the one hundred or so children enrolled in my Physical Developmental Clinic, nearly half tend to be more or less mentally retarded. Usually the parents of these children have received all kinds of information and advice concerning their youngsters—except in matters of sex.

In the very short time available, I talk about a number of sexual topics with groups of these parents in the hope that they will then be able to deal properly with their children. These sessions are always very well attended. The parents soon become more comfortable with the subject of sex and less anxious about their children's sexuality.

For background, I begin by talking about and illustrating our society's traditional, irrational attitude toward sex, especially as this attitude relates to children and perhaps even more especially as it may relate to mentally retarded and otherwise "different" children. Then I zero in on the following subjects.

MENSTRUATION

Education concerning menstruation is now widespread in schools and in girls' organizations. I therefore make only the following points concerning the subject, although of course other questions are sometimes raised. As with normal children, a retarded girl can begin to menstruate anywhere between ages nine and seventeen and still be within the "normal" range. Although many mentally retarded children are physically retarded as well, many are normal or even precocious in their physical development.

Parents should plan ahead for the girl's *probable* onset of menstruation, which will likely be after age nine and before age thirteen. The girl's ability to follow instructions should be a major factor in determining whether sanitary napkins or tampons should be used, the napkin being the simpler and probably preferable at least for a period of time. The teaching of cleanliness is, of course, important. However, parents should avoid giving the impression that the menstrual flow is "nasty" or especially objectionable in any way.

If the child is unable to understand the menstrual cycle, a simple assurance should be given that bleeding happens to all girls sometimes and "it's okay," and "it doesn't hurt you." This kind of instruction will need to be repeated often. Menstruation should not be viewed or talked of as a sickness. Generally speaking, the menstruating girl or woman can do whatever physical activities she is accustomed to doing when not menstruating. One of the best services that mothers can provide for their daughters is to be relaxed, accepting, and rational about their own menstrual periods as well as those of their daughters. A negative attitude on the part of the mother is very likely to give rise to unnecessary menstrual problems on the part of the daughter, retarded or normal.

PENIS ERECTIONS AND "WET DREAMS"

From a very early age, perhaps shortly after birth, boys tend to get erections periodically. Unless there is skin irritation or evidence of other medical problems, these should be viewed as entirely normal and natural—like any other bodily function. No boy, mentally retarded or otherwise, should be made to feel guilty for having erections, regardless of the circumstances. Erections are an automatic bodily adjustment on a par with the eye's adjustment to light.

One mentally retarded boy made a practice of stimulating his penis, literally pounding it black and blue so as to get erections intentionally. Among other things, this was an attention-getting device when with other boys. The approach used with him was to help him to learn to function more adequately as a member of the group so that he would not have to resort to such extreme measures to gain attention.

Between the ages of twelve and fifteen, many retarded boys, like normal boys, have spontaneous ejaculations (also called nocturnal emissions or wet dreams) while they are asleep. These should be expected; they are as natural as the girl's menstruations.

MASTURBATION

Everyone knows how badly masturbation is regarded in our tradition. It is recognized that sexual self-stimulation is not socially acceptable even though harmless and very possibly beneficial. If the child is capable of distinguishing between privately acceptable *versus* publicly acceptable behavior, he or she should be taught to confine such activity to places and times when they will not be disturbing to other people—just as he learns that urinating is done in the bathroom.

Skin irritations and poorly fitting clothing may cause what appear to be "excessive" masturbating. Before jumping to conclusions, the parent should check for evidence of skin rash and notice whether clothing is binding in the crotch. Very commonly, however, the child has simply not been provided with enough play activities to occupy his attention and his frequent self-stimulation is the equivalent of eating excessively when bored.

Sometimes, frequent masturbation and/or sexual self-stimulation are virtually forced on children. For example, an overactive as well as mentally retarded boy was regularly confined to his bedroom at an early hour in the evening. His mother became alarmed upon discovering that instead of going to sleep, William "played with himself." She did not bother to wonder whether the boy's bedtime was realistic, whether he had sufficient opportunity to engage in physical play that would encourage fatigue, etc.

For another example, one of our girls was punished at her boarding school by being confined to a bare room for extended periods without clothing or anything whatever to occupy her time. The school officials complained that she "masturbated a lot." Note that the school officials were virtually training the child to masturbate whenever she was bored.

SEX PLAY WITH OTHERS

If the opportunity exists, sex play is to be expected among children. It may be between children of like or unlike sex. In either case, parents tend to become very much upset and likely to administer punishment. Sex play by retarded children often tends to be viewed as abnormality added to abnormality. Such views need re-examination. Consider this.

A mongoloid boy and girl, well within the mentally retarded range, were playing actively together. In the course of playing, they had considerable physical contact, and while resting their contact continued and included a certain amount of caressing, the chest area and lower abdomen not being omitted. Professional observers at first felt compelled to identify this as undesirable behavior but were unable to convince themselves as to why. As a matter of fact, they finally decided that through physical play and contact the children were learning and demonstrating what was for them an exceptional level of communication ability and concern for each other's feelings and welfare. Of course, communication skills and social awareness are two of the major objectives in the training and education of the mentally retarded.

One of our retarded girls, age thirteen, was very normal by the usual physical criteria (except that she chose to crawl on her stomach or log-roll wherever she went). She was very much attracted sexually by her therapist, would attempt to unzipper and remove his trousers, and although she did not ordinarily talk at all, she managed to convey to him in words as well as gestures her desire to run about with him in the nude. Of course, the therapist could not possibly do as she wanted. But neither was he willing to rebuff her in such a way as to destroy his therapeutic efforts at treatment. Indeed, this sexual interest served as a communication bridge which presently made possible a diversion of energy to other activities. For example, although not nude, she would actually get to her feet and run with him.

In this case, the girl's sexual interest was at worst embarrassing. In a relatively few cases, however, the severely mentally retarded individual's efforts to express a sexual interest may constitute a serious hazard to others. For one example, a severely mentally retarded adolescent boy of approximately normal sexual development has acquired very strong, clawlike hands with which he can grasp, scratch, and twist painfully. Occasionally he grasps women's breasts and men's genitals without apparent awareness of the pain he inflicts. Reportedly, he has been physically punished for such behavior on repeated occasions but he does not seem to relate the punishment with the grasping and therefore persists in it.

Such behavior patterns in the young adult are usually beyond correction by parents or teachers and require the attention of psychologists, especially behavioral scientists. The earlier such clearly unacceptable behavior is noted and professional help sought, the better for all concerned.

OBSCENITY

Mildly mentally retarded children frequently have a strong interest in sexy pictures, poems, and jokes just as normal children generally do. Normal children usually learn how to express this interest so as not to be punished for it. The mentally retarded may be slower in developing such cunning or unable to develop it adequately at all. Moreover, the possession of "dirty" pictures and books, telling "dirty" stories and drawing "dirty" pictures may gain the child attention among his associates that he usually cannot get. For example, an elementary-school girl of low intelligence was the center of the little boys' attention because she would bring her father's "obscene" photographs to school to show them; a mentally retarded boy was the center of interest on the playground because he would show his brother's sexy cartoons to the boys; and a mildly retarded boy became something of a hero when he made a practice of boldly drawing sex cartoons and "dirty" words and pictures on lavatory and other walls. In due course, all of these children were caught and severely disciplined for these things.

Now, the first thing to remember about "obscenity" in the form of sexy pictures, songs, and literature is that no one has shown it to hurt the viewer or reader or to cause him or her to engage in antisocial activities. This is true in spite of the horrible things that "anti-smut" campaigners claim. Much of the dread of exposing the young to obscenity is based upon the assumption that it may stimulate them sexually and give rise to masturbation. All this made sense when it was supposed that masturbation causes diseases, death, and damnation. But it makes no sense at all today when masturbation is viewed as being harmless and very possibly beneficial in general.

If the mentally retarded find satisfaction in sexy pictures and so on, they are in a class with the millions who buy various magazines and watch television daily; and there is no rational basis for singling them out for persecution. I personally feel that "leagues of decency," anti-smut campaigners and the like would serve a much more useful purpose if they would spend their energy and time teaching their communities to treat the mentally retarded and other unfortunate people decently.

CONCLUSION

Sex education is one of the most neglected aspects of all of education. This makes a healthy adjustment very difficult for all children and youth, especially perhaps for the retarded and their parents. Parents should try to be as informed and rational about the sexual behavior of children as possible. They need to keep in mind the fact that we live in a society that is not very rational about sex and that therefore sexual adjustment tends to be difficult for everyone.

Traditionally, we have viewed the sex of the child, especially of the retarded child, as something that shouldn't be there, that must be eliminated, controlled, defeated. Perhaps a new day is coming. Perhaps we will begin to wonder why it is that sex is oftentimes one of the few things that people will respond to. Perhaps we will realize that we have been wasting a great resource in our educational and therapeutic efforts with people generally, including the retarded. Perhaps we will learn to use this energy of life and pleasure constructively in our rearing and education of the mentally retarded.

Part XI

Special Problems of Adolescence

34

What to Do About Late Adolescence

by JORDAN W. FINKELSTEIN, M.D.

The first signs of adolescence normally appear at any time from nine to seventeen years of age. While some children develop earlier, there are other boys and girls in whom the onset of maturity is delayed. These late developers often face a serious problem. They are concerned about their lack of progress and are frequently teased by their schoolmates when they have to undress for gym or swimming. The problem often becomes so severe that these children will refuse to take gym or participate in activities in which they must expose their nudity. Because of their embarrassment, they may withdraw from all group activities.

Fortunately, medicine has made enough progress today so that no child need suffer because of lack of sexual development. Treatment is now available for all cases regardless of the cause. However, before treatment is begun, it is important to know the exact cause of the delay. Since special tests and X rays may be needed to help in the diagnosis of delayed adolescence, it may be advisable to seek help at a nearby medical center where specially trained doctors, pediatric endocrinologists, will be available.

CAUSES FOR LACK OF SEXUAL DEVELOPMENT

By far the largest group with delayed sexual maturation are the "slow growers." *They have no glandular disturbance.* Almost all of these children are boys, although slow growth does occur in a few girls. Slow growers show no signs of sexual maturation at the expected times. Normally, most boys begin to mature at fourteen years of age, about one year later than most girls do. These children with normally delayed adolescence are often members of families in which a similar growth pattern has occurred. Sometimes brothers or sisters, fathers, cousins, and others have had the same problem and then have gone on to mature and raise families of their own.

Slow growers also face another problem—they are often short and have always been so. When one compares their height to that of other children the same age, one often finds that they are about a year or two behind their age-mates. As a result of their shortness, they may be open to further teasing.

Eventually, if no treatment is given to these boys and girls, they will experience the onset of sexual maturity. The usual growth spurt that accompanies adolescence will occur, and they will function as perfectly normal men and women and attain normal statures. However, because of the emotional problems associated with delayed puberty it often becomes necessary to step in and give nature a hand by treating these children for *short periods of time* with hormones. It is important for both parents and child to know that there is nothing wrong with the child's sex glands except that they are a little sleepy, so to speak, and that all the doctor is doing by treatment is giving these lazy glands a nudge.

There are very few children who fail to mature as a result of a glandular disturbance, but a few cases do exist. It is important to know when this is the case, since it will greatly influence the type and time of treatment that should be given. One such group consists entirely of girls, all of whom are short, never becoming taller than five feet. They may have other noticeable problems such as "webbed" or "kitten" necks, wide-set eyes, receding chins and, sometimes, heart conditions. At the usual time of adolescence they may develop some sexual hair, but they do not develop breasts, nor do they menstruate.

These girls are born either without ovaries (the organs that produce the ova or eggs and make the female hormones), or with very small rudimentary ovaries which cannot function normally. Doctors can now make this diagnosis easily by a few special urine tests, and by examining under a microscope some of the cells scraped from the cheek walls inside the mouth. In some unusual cases an operation may be necessary to be absolutely certain of the condition.

It is necessary for girls with this condition to have their children by adoption, since they cannot make their own ova, but since they have a normal womb and vagina they can be made, by treatment, to have normal menstruation. This is important for psychological as well as medical reasons. They can also develop normal breasts under treatment. They can have perfectly normal sexual relations and sexual desires. They must, however, continue to take treatment until the usual time of the menopause, or change of life.

Another group of children consists of boys who do not mature sexually. These boys may develop some sexual hair, but they do not experience any other sexual development. Their testicles (the glands that produce the sperms and male hormones) are defective in their development. These children, unlike the girls previously mentioned, do not have any other problems. They grow normally but may become excessively tall if treatment is not given.

At the usual time of adolescence, the testicles remain infantile in size and do not mature and produce male hormones. Again, a few special tests will help the doctor to make this diagnosis and to institute proper treatment. These boys must become fathers either by adoption, or by donor insemination of their wives (with the semen of another male), but they are perfectly able to function normally in sexual intercourse. They have normal sexual desires and are capable of a normal marital relationship. They too, must take treatment until old age.

Some boys and girls have a disorder of the pituitary gland, which is often called the "master gland" because it controls many of the other glands in the body. The pituitary is a pea-sized structure which sits beneath the base of the brain. If it does not secrete enough of the pituitary hormones, many of the other organs in the body do not function properly.

Children with this condition are all markedly short (having the height of a child three or more years younger than themselves), and they may have underactive thyroid and adrenal glands in addition to underactive sex glands. Many complicated tests are necessary for the doctor to make this diagnosis. Even in the rare instances of underactive pituitaries, treatment can be given to promote sexual development and maturation, as well as to correct some of the other deficiencies.

The last group of children are those who have had serious operations and in whom it was necessary to remove the sex glands and their related organs. These children do not present any *diagnostic* problem since the doctor will know what has happened and why they are not developed sexually. Again, with the proper treatment they can develop sexually and function as normally as all the other children. They must have their children by adoption.

Regardless of the cause of lack of sexual development, treatment is now available for all those who need it. Once the cause of the lack of development is ascertained, the doctor will know when to begin treatment, how long it should be given, and what type of treatment should be used. Most problems can be solved by taking one pill a day, but sometimes a course of injections may be necessary for a short period of time.

The biggest problem in treatment occurs in the group of children who are slow growers. One of the effects of treatment is to speed up growth and bone development, and since these children are usually short it is best to wait as long as possible before starting treatment, which will allow them to attain the greatest possible height. Since the rate of bone maturation caused by treatment is more rapid than the rate of growth in height, children who are treated too soon may not be able to attain their expected height.

However, if the psychological problems which often accompany late sexual development become pressing, it may be more advantageous to begin treatment at the sacrifice of a few inches in height. The doctor's advice, and the help of a psychologist specially trained in these problems, may be particularly useful. The children in this group are fortunate in that they have to be treated only for a short period of time—usually a few months—and then they can wait until their own glands become active and take up the job of maintaining sexual maturity.

In girls, *estrogen,* the normal female sex hormone, may be given in the form of pills taken once a day. In boys a six-week course of injections twice a week with a substance called *gonadotropin,* which may stimulate the "sleepy" sex glands, may be used. Alternatively, *testosterone,* the male sex hormone, may be given in a series of injections once a month, or as pills taken once a day.

The six week course of injections of gonadotropin can be used only in those boys who are slow growers. If the sexual infantilism is due to any of the other previously mentioned causes, then testosterone is the only treatment which is successful. Once it is decided to start treatment, the doctor will prescribe the necessary pills or injections.

In girls who receive treatment with estrogens the following changes will occur. Breasts will develop to whatever size they would have been if the body were making its own hormones. One must remember that, even by giving more and more hormones, doctors cannot do more than nature intended. Women with small breasts cannot make them grow by taking extra estrogen pills, or by applying hormone creams to their breasts. Just as some people are tall and others are short, some women have large breasts and others small.

After several months of treatment, menstruation will occur if the womb is present. When this happens, the doctor will change treatment to three weeks on and one week off pills so that regular menstruation will occur each month. In this respect, the women who are taking pills have an advantage over other women since they can control the time that they have their periods by the way they take their pills. If, because of a vacation or an important weekend, they wish to miss their period for one month, they can take the pills in such a way as to skip their period. However, this should only be done under the doctor's supervision as serious problems with excessive bleeding may otherwise occur later.

Other changes, including the appearance of pubic and underarm hair and the rounding out of the body to womanly curves will also occur. Acne may appear and this should be treated as the doctor advises. A growth spurt will also occur, the extent of which will be determined by the state of bone development at the time treatment is begun.

If treatment is begun too early, growth may be rapid for a while but it will soon cease, because the bones mature and the growing ends close over more rapidly than growth in height occurs. For this reason the exact time to begin treatment should be carefully supervised by the doctor. A few X rays of the bones are very helpful in deciding when to start treatment. Only those girls who are slow growers can bear their own children. The others will all have to have their children by adoption.

In boys who receive hormone treatment, many changes will occur. The penis will begin to grow and will reach its normal adult size. Here again one must realize that different men have different-sized penises, just as women have different-sized breasts. By giving more and more hormones, one cannot make the penis become any larger than nature intended it to be.

Pubic and underarm hair will grow, as will the beard. The voice will begin to crack, and eventually a deep masculine voice will be present. Acne may occur for which the doctor can prescribe treatment. If the testicles have not developed normally, then no enlargement of these organs will occur. If the testicles are absent or remain very tiny, artificial testicles, made of a plastic material, may be placed in the scrotum by a simple operation, if the patient desires this.

If the problem is just that of a slow grower, then the doctor will want to stop treatment at certain intervals to do some further tests and to see if the sex glands can go ahead by themselves. If the testicles begin to enlarge, treatment is usually no longer necessary, for the body is ready to take up its normal work of maintaining sexual maturity.

Along with sexual maturation, a growth spurt will also occur. As was previously mentioned, bone maturation occurs more rapidly than growth in height. This is especially true in boys, since the male hormone causes more rapid bone maturation than does the female hormone. So again, while it may be desirable to start treatment early, bone maturation should be measured by X rays, and psychological factors balanced against the probable loss of several inches in height.

All of these boys can marry and have perfectly normal sexual relations. Only those boys who were slow growers will be able to produce children of their own. The other boys must have their children by adoption or by donor insemination of their wives.

EMOTIONAL PROBLEMS INVOLVED

Finally, a word should be said about the emotional problems that can accompany the physical problems. These boys and girls usually take a good deal of teasing from their friends and may become sensitive about their problem. Since treatment is readily available, these emotional problems are usually short-lived. However, it is important for a teen-ager to have a good knowledge of the facts of life, and of his condition, from both his parents and his physician, in order to understand the problem with which he or she is faced.

In addition, privacy in the home and at school in the gym may be desirable. For the most part, however, the child will benefit from being treated as a normal individual, and not pampered or made an invalid. Even though there may be some permanent abnormality in sexual development, the major manifestations can be corrected with treatment.

Preparation to face the problem of eventual inability to bear their own children may be begun with these patients even at an early age. The topic needs to be approached with tact, common sense, and lack of emotionalism. Most children find it easier to face the facts than—having perhaps smelled a rat—to fight uncertainty and the unknown. Moreover, if they grow up anticipating a family by adoption or by donor insemination, then they have no sudden letdown and shock in adolescence or young adulthood. In cases where the problem of emotional adjustment becomes severe, it may be desirable to secure assistance from a psychologist or psychiatrist who is competent in glandular disorders and sexual maturation.

35

What Should Parents Do About Pornography?

by ISADORE RUBIN, PH.D.

NO CAUSE-AND-EFFECT RELATIONSHIP BETWEEN PORNOGRAPHY AND UNACCEPTABLE CONDUCT HAS BEEN PROVEN

These days, when any group wants to impose a policy of censorship, they always use as their reason "the protection of our youth." So much has appeared in the popular press about the pernicious effects of erotic literature or "pornography"—a term, incidentally, that nobody, including the justices of the United States Supreme Court, has ever really been able to define—on young people that parents are naturally deeply concerned. Because of the emotionalism with which this whole subject is charged, it is worthwhile to examine carefully the evidence by which different groups come to the conclusion that erotic literature is extremely dangerous.

We can disregard groups that base their appeals on ignorance and on a conscious or unconscious feeling that all sexuality is "dirty" and evil. Let us turn to the statement issued by the Committee on Public Health of the New York Academy of Medicine, which has called for federal action to protect young people against erotic and "salacious" literature.

Their statement begins by admitting that it is "difficult, if not impossible," to prove that there is a cause-and-effect relationship between erotic literature and unacceptable conduct. Then they go on to assert that there has been a sharp increase of VD, especially among teen-age youth, and that the rate of illegitimacy is climbing. They admit that it is impossible to prove any connection between the rise in the sale of salacious literature and the rise in VD and illegitimacy. But they then go on to make the following statement: "It can be asserted, however, that the perusal of erotic literature has the potentiality of inciting some young persons to enter into illicit sex relations and thus of leading them into promiscuity."

Incidentally, it is extremely illogical and even foolish to try to establish a statistical relationship between promiscuity, illegitimacy, or VD and the extent of the circulation of erotic materials. For example, the nine years following the publication of the first Kinsey Report probably saw a great leap forward in the extent of erotic material published; yet in those same years venereal disease figures declined from their highest point in our history to our lowest! Also, in the years 1957 to 1963—years when probably the greatest leap forward in the extent of erotic publications occurred—the rate of illegitimacy declined among teen-agers between the ages of fifteen to nineteen, the only age group where figures showed a decline.

Actually, no one knows exactly what will be the effect of any picture, book, film, or newspaper account on a particular person. In his book analyzing movie censorship, *New York Times* critic Murray Schumach made the following telling point about what may incite a person to action:

Who shall say whether a movie about crime will "inspire others with desire for imitation"?

A classic example is on file at the offices of the movie censors. There one can find a clipping about a youth who murdered his teen-aged date while they were necking in a car shortly after seeing a movie. The film was Walt Disney's *Snow White and the Seven Dwarfs.* The censors shudder at what might have been the public reaction if the picture had been something like *Anatomy of a Murder,* in which rape and murder figured so prominently.

And in an address given before the New York Society for Ethical Culture in July, 1966, Leader Leonard Mandelbaum cited the following interesting cases from court records:

There *are* two recorded recorded histories of violent sexual criminal acts that were committed after the offender came in touch with material clearly not obscene. In the first case, Heinrich Pomeranke, a rapist and a mass slayer of women in Germany, was prompted to a series of deeds by Cecil B. DeMille's "The Ten Commandments." . . . During the scene of the Jewish women dancing around the golden calf all the doubts of his life became clear. Women were the source of the world's trouble. And it was his mission to punish them and to execute them. Leaving the theater he immediately slew the first victim in the park nearby.

Then there is John George Hague, the British vampire who sucked his victims' blood through soda straws, and dissolved their drained bodies in acid baths. He first had his murder-inciting dreams and his vampire longings from watching the voluptuous procedure, of all things, of an Anglican high church service.

Certainly no group would ask that films like *Snow White and the Seven Dwarfs* and the *Ten Commandments,* or attendance at church services, be banned because they may possibly incite a disturbed character to some kind of violence.

Just what relationship has been established by any scientific studies between pornographic literature and delinquency or sex offenses on the part of youth? The clear answer is "absolutely none!" Let us turn to the bibliography entitled "Pornographic Literature and Its Relationship to Sex Offenses" in the U.S. Senate Subcommittee report on its hearings on pornography and delinquency published in 1956. At the beginning of the bibliography, we find this apologetic but unambiguous admission: "There are no studies on the relationship of pornographic literature to sexual offense. . . ."

Eight years later when the Russell Sage Foundation published its important *Review of Child Development Research,* not a single reference could be mentioned in it to any study on the effect of pornography. And in a recent book by Columbia University professor Eli Ginzburg on values and ideals of youth, H. B. Warburton, a former General Counsel for the U.S. Post Office Department, declared: "It must be baldly stated that there appears to have been no basic sociological or psychiatric research done upon the question of whether exposure to obscene, or otherwise objectionable, material leads to misbehavior."

There is some indication from recent research that pornography probably does *not* have any real effect in leading to sex offenses. The latest Kinsey volume, *Sex Offenders,* found that men in prison for sex offenses seem to have read less pornography than men in prison for nonsex offenses.

It is worth noting that no major group of psychiatrists or psychologists has ever agreed with the position taken by the New York Academy of Medicine. In 1966, for example, the New Jersey Committee for the Right to Read presented to the governor the findings of a survey it had conducted among 934 psychiatrists and psychologists of that state. Almost 90 per cent of those surveyed opposed censorship laws to exclude sex literature from stores and libraries. Over 86 per cent did not believe such exclusion would encourage healthier attitudes toward sex in young people. All but a handful denied that they had any normal patients who had been provoked to delinquent acts by sexually oriented literature, and two thirds thought that such literature might cut down on delinquent behavior by serving as a substitute outlet. In answering the questionnaire, many added personal comments. One clinical psychologist remarked that in twelve years of practice with emotionally disturbed and delinquent children he had not seen a single case where a child was harmed by reading pornographic material. Another suggested that "sexually stimulating materials" might help certain persons to develop a normal sexual drive.

However, there is one other aspect of pornography that should not be overlooked. A great deal of pornography emphasizes not the erotic aspects but the aspects of aggression, violence and sadism. Although exposure to such literature might not lead to misbehavior, for youngsters who have still not achieved a mature sexual identity it is not a desirable preparation for a future interpersonal sex and love relationship.

Sexual behavior and aggressive behavior may be especially closely related in the nervous system, biologists have indicated, and cruelty in relation to sexual behavior may be easily conditioned. If this be so, parents and teachers should find ways of immunizing youngsters against any possible ill effects of sadistic literature.

Can they do this by trying to make the sale of such pornography illegal? The answer is "no," for hard-core pornography, which circulates in millions of copies, has long been illegal. We could not possibly stop its flow without a censorship and repressive atmosphere so drastic that our traditional freedoms of speech would have to disappear. Surely, no one would want a complete reorganization of democracy to prevent a harm that is as yet only "possible" and may not amount to anything serious even if established.

Besides, the greatest tie-up between sex and violence is not found in pornography. It is found in dozens of films like the popular James Bond ones, or the stories by Mickey Spillane, or the popular television programs, or the vivid accounts in tabloid newspapers which play up the sensational details of each new sex and murder scandal while editorially lamenting the evils of pornography.

The best way to protect our youngsters is to provide them as early as possible with sound and worthwhile education about sex, to teach them at an early age about the rich meaning of sexuality, and to provide enough information so that they need not turn to pornography to satisfy their curiosity.

36

What Adolescents Should Know About the Law

by HUGO G. BEIGEL, PH.D.

More than 70 per cent of all girls who are brought before a court as juvenile delinquents are accused of sexual offenses. Yet it is highly probable that most teen-age girls at one time or another have done exactly what almost half (43 per cent) of the "sexual delinquents" did. For the "crime" of the girls in this group was that they were seen petting in a motion-picture theater, or in a more intimate situation in a car parked on a back road.

Most youngsters know, of course, that their adventures must not be revealed at home. Their parents would make a fuss. But otherwise they make no secret of their clandestine enjoyment. Why should they, they ask? Everybody does it, and anyway, it's nobody's business. To them, the prohibitions surrounding their sexual activities are just another bunch of "don'ts" which parents hand out so lavishly to their children. What they do not realize, however, is that in the eyes of the law they are no longer children.

And here we come to the point. If ignorance can get young people into such serious conflicts with the law and the courts do not accept it as an excuse, then this ignorance must be attacked. It is not enough to rave against the irrationality of some parts of our sex legislation.

Many adolescents do not realize that they are violating a law. Indeed, their own evaluation of what is more and what is less in keeping with virtue is sometimes so naïve that it produces a situation fraught with irony. Thus, one girl apprehended in rather indiscreet circumstances was described as particularly depraved by the judge—and penalized accordingly—because she did and tolerated what some of the law books call perverted acts, including sodomy. Yet the girl had consented to them because her moral concepts forbade her to "go all the way" and she felt that she owed her disappointed boyfriend some compensation.

Another case, in its way equally tragic, is that of a college student who, in a public washroom, was approached by a man with a homosexual proposition. When the boy responded, the tempter flashed a badge. He was a police officer. Fortunately, the judge was a reasonable man; he dismissed the "offender" with a warning. However, the incident came to the knowledge of the college authorities. They were not unreasonable either. But since the young man had chosen high-school teaching for his vocation, the question arose whether it was advisable to let him—a man now under suspicion of homosexuality—continue his career.

This young man, intelligent though he was, did not feel that by apparently accepting the detective's suggestion he was committing a punishable act, nor was he interested in the homosexual contact itself. He was simply curious. Curious to see what this man would try next. It was an adventure and he was sure that he could at any moment extricate himself and go home richer for a real life experience. It was an experience all right, but one entailing serious consequences. There is no doubt that this young man would have acted with better judgment if he had known that he was tangling with the law and that the law does not exempt those who violate it in their quest for knowledge.

Nor does it exempt those who believe that love is an entirely private affair. One man sought counseling because he was in a predicament. He was just over twenty and about two years before he had fallen in love with a girl who at that time was not yet fifteen. He had intended to marry her but when the relationship had lasted for a year she got tired of him. He did not want to let her go. In his immature wisdom he decided on a course of action that would tie her to him forever. He would no longer wait but would have complete sex relations with her. When the girl visited him next time, he did not stop where they usually did but made the planned attempt. After initial resistance, the girl yielded. Apparently impressed by either the lover's attitude or by the novel experience, she continued the relationship.

For another six months, the young man was happy. But from the legal point of view he had committed a whole series of offenses: contributing to the delinquency of a minor, fornication, and to top it all, statutory rape. He had never thought of it that way. His love, his need for affection, and his fear of losing her were, he felt, noble reasons, and all that had happened was only her and his business. When it was explained to him that it was not, he was flabbergasted and only replied: "But she didn't mind." This man, too, would probably have controlled his passion if he had known that there are barriers more dangerously spiked than the rules of proper behavior.

It is true that some of these laws completely disregard physical needs and psychological drives and that their enforcement can with more justification be called a "crime against nature" than can the acts which are described under this phrase in the statutes. One indication of this is the fact that only a small number of those brought before a court are ever involved in any other kind of delinquency.

Yet in spite of all rational arguments, the law has a way of asserting itself that cannot and must not be overlooked. Under sufficient pressure, it will be brought up to the standards of a rational reality some day.

But what until then? If lack of knowledge is one of the causes that brings teen-agers into conflict with the law, then this knowledge must be conveyed to them. And that is undoubtedly the task of sex education. Unless parents want to leave that part of sex education to the police and the various reform and penal institutions, they had better give it as long as there is still time. (It goes without saying, of course, that such information should be given in a natural, nonfrightening kind of way.)

Sex education can no longer concern itself only with the biological aspect of reproduction. It must be broadened. It must be supplemented with information about the sex mores in our society. The educational agencies must make it clear that in our culture sex activities are not merely a private matter between individuals and their consciences. Adolescents are dealing not only with the easily circumvented prohibitions of their parents, but with an impersonal and inflexible force, the law.

Will that help? Will it stop boys and girls from seeking relief for urges which in adolescence reach their maximum intensity? Probably not in all cases; but very likely in those where they act only from exuberance, braggadocio, curiosity or a misunderstood obligation. How often do girls give in to the urgings of a boy not because they feel driven, but merely because they believe that this is expected of them? Armed with the pertinent information, a boy will know that whatever fun he gets out of practicing his artistic talents on the wall of a public building or from peeping into a window where a woman is undressing, or from making remarks of a sexual nature within earshot of prissy females, it is not worth the trouble that he must expect if he is caught. Young people must be taught, in the interests of their own protection, that our society tolerates few demonstrations of affection in public and even penalizes many forms of sexual activity which are seemingly a private matter.

37

Alcohol and Teen-Age Sex

by HERMAN E. KRIMMEL, M.S.S.W.

Adolescence is a period of budding sexual drives striving for expression. Adults are naturally concerned about the behavior of teen-agers. Their alarm is increased by sensational reports about the rise in teen-age drinking and they become convinced that alcohol hastens the sexual reaction between boy and girl. Unfortunately, it is difficult to separate truth from guesswork. There has been considerable research into teen-age sexual activity—perhaps more research than activity. There has been little study of teen-age drinking habits. However, there has been no end of guesswork about both, and their relationship to each other.

For example, unwed motherhood is frequently blamed on the bourbon bottle. This may happen occasionally, but there is no real evidence to go on. It is true, of course, that many husbandless mothers blame their pregnancies on alcohol. But, as Professor Leontine Young observes in her highly regarded book *Out of Wedlock,* most of the girls knew the fathers of their children only casually.

She writes:

They tell you that they remember taking a drink—interestingly it is rarely more than one drink—and then know nothing until they wake up to discover that the sexual act has transpired in their psychological absence. Still other girls, unconsciously, if not consciously, aware that taking a drink is an action that in their minds could lead to a weakening of inhibition and hence to a possible sexual act, say only that they remember having a non-alcoholic drink such as Coca Cola. Their explanation is always that the man must have put knockout drops in the drink.

Concludes Professor Young:

They are invariably deluding themselves, and it is reasonable to believe they would have had the "blackout" even without the liquor.

All this is not intended to minimize the dangers of mixing sex and alcohol. Alcohol is primarily a *depressant*. Strangely enough, however, its *initial* action has the effect of *stimulation*. The first few drinks act on nerve centers of the brain which control the inhibitions. These controls are depressed and the inhibited impulses are released. Thus the quiet person becomes noisy; the wallflower begins to dance. Laughter and gaiety replace solemnity. This is why liquor has been man's favorite social lubricant for centuries. Obviously, this kind of stimulation can result in the breakthrough of adolescent sex drives.

Fortunately, however, there are many checks on this danger. One is the awareness of the teen-agers themselves. A few years ago a group of high-school boys and girls were questioned in Montreal. Most felt that a girl who gets drunk on a date is a "fool playing with fire." The students agreed that she puts herself in a situation which she might not be able to handle. This kind of awareness has a built-in braking quality. Moreover, inhibitions that come from firmly held values can be stretched, but not easily broken. The values acquired from a healthy family life and a sound sex education are a good bet to survive the kind of drinking that is done by most teen-agers.

There is a widespread tendency to confuse the growing *popularity* of teen-age drinking with the amount consumed. *Although there has never been a truly scientific nationwide survey of adolescent drinking, there have been several good local studies.* There is general agreement that more teen-agers are experimenting with alcoholic beverages at an earlier age than in previous generations. Most of the teen-agers surveyed, however, were not *drinkers* in the accepted sense of the word, and almost none got really drunk. (One in ten in Michigan described themselves as drinkers, but allowance must be made for bragging. Or, as a Cleveland high-school girl said to me recently: "The guys like to tell you how crocked they got, but no one really believes them.")

Moreover, it should be emphasized that a discussion of teen-age drinking seldom involves hard liquor. In all the studies, most of the drinking was confined to beer or wine. Both have low alcoholic content and are not likely to be consumed in quanties that promote sexual orgies.

None of the studies of teen-age drinking discusses alcohol and sexual activity. They do reveal that some adolescents find that drinking "makes dating easier." But even that purpose is not given primary importance. The image of the teen-ager so aflame with desire that he coaxes his date into a drunken stupor in order to have intercourse with her is an exaggeration. Drinking for many adolescents is almost an end in itself rather than a path to easy sex relations. Christopher Sower of the University of Michigan describes it as "a means of dissolving adolescent status and demonstrating adult status." The use of alcohol to achieve grown-up *status* rather than *sexual conquest* is not new. Many of those who grew up in the late twenties or early thirties, during Prohibition, can recall youthful small sips that really gave the illusion of having made it into manhood in a big way.

However, even excessive drinking has its safeguards. As we have seen, alcohol is essentially a depressant; in excess, it tends to subdue sexual activity. In many males it may cause temporary impotence. As the porter in *Macbeth* said, "It provokes the desire but takes away the performance." One young man who was a patient at the Cleveland Center on Alcoholism had started to drink during his teens because he was afraid of girls and turned to alcohol for courage. However, a few drinks failed to provide the necessary courage; a few more washed away his interest in females entirely.

When measured against the lurid newspaper and magazine accounts of drinking and sexual promiscuity among teen-agers, this report may sound unreal. The accuracy of many of these sensational stories is well documented. There *are* cellar clubs in many cities where drinking and sex go hand in hand. But the problems of these youngsters do not originate in alcohol. Their drinking and their sex behavior are both expressions of emotional deformities.

Safety does not depend on prohibition. It comes from healthy standards. It is essential that those growing into adulthood should learn the difference between use and abuse of *both* sex and alcohol. Sex is, of course, a vital part of the life of every well-adjusted human being and should be one of its most exhilarating experiences. The drinking of alcohol beverages is certainly, while not essential, a pleasant social custom enjoyed by a majority of adults. The two are not necessarily related.

38

Hazards of Youthful Marriage

by CURTIS E. AVERY

You can have almost any statistic you want, to prove that the rate of teen-age marriage is increasing in the United States and that the increase is causing problems. It all depends on what magazines or Sunday supplements you read. But, just to furnish a reasonably accurate point of departure, let's say: (1) If the present trend continues, more than half of the teen-age females in the United States will have been married at least once by the year 1970. (2) Again, if the present trend continues until 1970, 25 per cent of all the marriages in that year will unite boys and girls younger than twenty years.

Don't believe everything you read about the awful results of this explosion, especially in terms of statistics. But you can safely accept the fact that there are more divorces, desertions, and unhappy marriages among teen-agers than among older couples. And you can accept the fact that, for various reasons, there are many problems of child welfare among children of teen-age parents that don't loom so large among other children. And it's true that there is a shockingly high incidence of terminated education for intelligent and even brilliant boys and girls who elect marriage instead of college or graduate school—at a time when the country desperately needs more and more highly educated men and women.

These are the facts which worry social scientists—indeed they worry everybody. The problems of teen-age marriage are not merely those which individual couples encounter. They are problems which all of us share; because divorce, marital unhappiness, inadequate child rearing, and unrealized intellectual potentials affect every one of us in countless ways.

THREE KINDS OF TEEN-AGE MARRIAGE

Now, before we go any further, let's clear up a point that causes much confusion in all the endless discussion about the evils of early marriage. *There are three kinds of teen-age marriage lumped together in the statistics.* One is the "traditional" marriage. It is just like the marriages we extol for older couples in all apparent respects save the age of the bride and groom. The boy and girl are in love—or sincerely believe they are—and want to get married for the same reasons their parents and grandparents had. They may not have parental approval and they may not be "ready" for marriage. But then, lots of twenty-five-year-old couples aren't ready either. The important fact about these marriages, however, is that the bride is not pregnant at the time of marriage.

Then, there is the "quasi-traditional" marriage, which is just like the first kind of marriage except for one thing: *the bride is pregnant.* But the couple have the same sincere, although perhaps misguided, desire for marriage and home. These are not forced marriages, despite the fact that the bride is pregnant.

Finally, there are the forced marriages. The bride is pregnant. She, or her parents, or both sets of parents insist on marriage even though nobody really wants it save as a way to avoid social disapproval of "unwed motherhood."

Various studies indicate that, in anywhere from 31 to 81 per cent of the marriages involving two high-school students, the bride is premaritally pregnant. The variation depends on the community or state in which the study was made. Let's simply agree that premarital pregnancy exists more frequently among teen-age couples than among older couples. But we do not know, and have no way of finding out accurately, what percentage of teen-age marriages involving premarital pregnancy are forced or "shotgun" marriages.

This is important because there is no doubt that the forced marriage is much more likely to end in divorce or desertion than the marriage eagerly desired by both partners, whether or not the bride is pregnant, and yet the statistics on divorce and desertion cannot take this into account.

The point of all this becomes apparent when we consider the problems of teen-age marriage we set out to discuss. We have to be sure we are talking about *these* problems rather than those involved in forced marriage. There may be more forced marriages among teen-agers than among older couples, and the associated problems may be more acute; *but they are still problems of forced marriage rather than problems of teen-age marriage.* By the same token, we need to think twice about *unforced* marriages involving pregnant brides. Again, these are apparently more frequent among teen-age couples than among older couples, and the problems created by premarital pregnancy are perhaps more poignant than those of older premaritally pregnant brides. But basically they are problems of premarital pregnancy and not problems of teen-age marriage unless you want to make premarital pregnancy and teen-age marriage virtually synonymous. And that is what people have apparently done.

MAJOR PROBLEMS OF TEEN-AGE MARRIAGE

The first major problem of teen-age marriage is the general public attitude toward it; and this attitude seems to be conditioned by the assumption that if a couple under age twenty get married the girl is pregnant—or, at least, the couple have "been up to *something.*" Teen-age marriage and "immorality" have been linked somehow. Since we are opposed to immorality, we must be opposed to teen-age marriage—it is offensive. "If thine eye offend thee pluck it out." So, we have tried to rid ourselves of the problems of teen-age marriage by imposing penalties and punishment on youthful couples.

Perhaps this is best illustrated by the attitudes and actions of some school boards and school administrators. Frequently their policies call for expulsion of married students. Others deny them membership in honor societies, and participation in extracurricular activities. One nationwide survey found that 7 per cent of the superintendents recommended segregation of married students at lunchtime, 22 per cent advised against married students participating in student affairs, and 91 per cent said that pregnant wives should be summarily dismissed from school, whether the pregnancy was premarital or postmarital.

But, despite these punitive measures, the teen-age marriage rate has continued to grow in most states, along with the rate of problems associated with early marriage. On the one hand, it seems pretty clear that penalties and prohibitions won't stop the trend; and on the other hand one suspects that they may create or intensify the problems they were designed to prevent. Remember, these problems have to do with marriage failure, welfare of children and continued education.

All marriages, at whatever age, certainly involve problems of interpersonal and social adjustment. But teen-age marriages are more vulnerable to the impact of these problems if the couples are subjected to what amounts to calculated ostracism or specially contrived penalties. Thus, perhaps the high rate of divorce, desertion, and separation in early marriages results not so much from a built-in factor involving the age of the couples as from the attitude of elders who disapprove. The first major problem of teen-age marriage is that of living in a society that, theoretically at least, disapproves of these marriages and penalizes them from the start in many overt and covert ways.

Our real concern should be to help these marriages succeed rather than administering punishment in the vain hope that others may be prevented. The moral issues involved in *some* of our teen-age marriages are not to be disregarded; but they should not be magnified to the extent that all teen-age marriages are tarred with the brush of illicit sex. And they should be dealt with for what they are—moral issues, not teen-age marriage issues.

However, this leads us smack into the second problem of teen-age marriage—an area about which few commentators care to write frankly and honestly. In a word, this basic problem is *children*. The many difficulties encountered by teen-age couples seem almost always to involve offspring in one way or another.

To most teen-agers, even when their marriage is subsidized, so to speak, by parents or others, the economic realities are pretty grim for the simple reason that they—or the husband—cannot possibly have reached a very high level of earning. This problem involves all teen-age couples who have not carefully and realistically planned their parenthood, whether or not premarital pregnancy is involved. As far as teen-age marriage is concerned, conventional morality need not enter into the picture. A teen-age couple who bring a child into the world ten months after marriage under conditions that are harmful to their own happiness and welfare and inescapably detrimental to the best development and growth of their child are just as immoral as the couple who produce a child four or six months after marriage.

So, there are two major problems of teen-age marriage—problems that concern us all in light of the increasing rate of these marriages. One has to do with our futile attempt to stop the trend of youthful marriage by imposing penalties and punishments which only lessen the chances of success for these marriages. The other has to do with the ever-insistent matter of planned parenthood.

The solution to both problems is to be found only in education—classroom education and home education working together. The first problem can be solved only by preaching the doctrine and teaching the bases of marriage readiness, regardless of age. The second problem is trickier. Probably we cannot teach birth-control techniques to unmarried teen-agers—although the new contraceptive pills may make this only an academic problem anyway. But we can teach the virtues of planned parenthood. And this approach, if it can be successfully applied, may have more success than the moral or the punitive approaches so frequently used in arguments about teen-age marriage.